25 LOW-COST Biology Investigations

Joel Beller

illustrated by Dawn Laurel Nelson

J. WESTON
WALCH
PUBLISHER

PORTLAND, MAINE

User's Guide
to
Walch Reproducible Books

As part of our general effort to provide educational materials which are as practical and economical as possible, we have designated this publication a "reproducible book." The designation means that purchase of the book includes purchase of the right to limited reproduction of all pages on which this symbol appears:

Here is the basic Walch policy: We grant to individual purchasers of this book the right to make sufficient copies of reproducible pages for use by all students of a single teacher. This permission is limited to a single teacher, and does not apply to entire schools or school systems, so institutions purchasing the book should pass the permission on to a single teacher. Copying of the book or its parts for resale is prohibited.

Any questions regarding this policy or requests to purchase further reproduction rights should be addressed to:

Permissions Editor
J. Weston Walch, Publisher
321 Valley Street • P. O. Box 658
Portland, Maine 04104-0658

1   2   3   4   5   6   7   8   9   10
ISBN 0-8251-1953-7

Contents

Acknowledgments

My special thanks to Susan Appel, assistant principal of the science department of Townsend Harris High School in Flushing, New York, for her assistance with the roach investigations, and to Odile Garcia and her Science on the Road enrichment class who field-tested a number of the investigations, including those on aquatic oil spills. Their suggestions and comments were extremely helpful.

I also want to thank Paul Rosendahl, laboratory specialist at I.S. 227 (the Louis Armstrong Middle School) in Elmhurst, New York, for his help with and suggestions for the dandelion and respiration investigations.

Introduction

This book has its origins in the recent economic recession and the resulting budget crunch that was imposed upon almost every school district in the United States. Paramount, and particularly vexing to me, was the issue of providing meaningful laboratory experiences for 30 biology classes, given a supply budget of $200 for the school year. I had to either deny the students the opportunity to participate in hands-on biological experiences or find and/or devise biological investigations that cost little or no money. The latter option was the only viable one. And that is what this book is about.

Some of the investigations in this book involve organisms that are free for the taking, organisms you see almost constantly but ignore. For example, dandelions, which are used in eight investigations, can be found during their growing seasons in both vacant lots and lawns, in cities as well as rural and suburban areas. Spider webs are also free and easily found in many locales. Furthermore, the webs can be investigated without destroying them. Land crustaceans inhabit moist environments and can be released after the investigation into their oxygen consumption. This highlights another positive aspect of these investigations: In most cases the examined organism is returned to its natural environment unharmed. Good use is made of students, their families, and their friends as experimental organisms. These, too, are returned to their environments unharmed. A few inexpensive organisms will have to be purchased from a scientific supply company; two of these are vinegar eels and preserved spiders.

With the exception of microscopes (needed for a few of the investigations), all equipment can be found either at home or in the science storeroom. Supplies are inexpensive and most are universally found in school science supply rooms throughout the nation. Lugol's iodine, salt, and vegetable oil are typical of the expendable materials that will be required.

The types of investigations in this book are a mix of cookbook recipe and open-ended inquiry. For each investigation, Teacher Resource Notes are provided to ensure that the activity will be successful, rewarding, and educationally profitable.

All investigations have been tested using biology and life science students in a number of New York City high schools and middle schools. The youngsters were able to carry out these investigations and found them exciting and worthwhile. I am sure your students will have similar experiences.

—*Joel Beller*

Teacher Resource Notes

Dandelion Lab #1:
Inducing and Observing the Growth of Pollen Tubes from Dandelion Pollen Grains

SUMMARY. In this lab students observe, record, and draw the growth of pollen tubes in a sugar solution. While carrying out this investigation, students will have a lot of free time between half-hour observations. Therefore, it would be wise to presoak the pollen grains for 20 to 25 minutes prior to the time the students enter the laboratory.

Because the pollen tube growth can be seen with magnifying lenses and hand-held illuminated field microscopes that magnify 30X or less, this laboratory research could be assigned as a home activity. Each student could be given an optical instrument, a small medicinal dropper bottle of sucrose solution, a slide, and lens paper to take home. Some schools require a monetary deposit from the parent to cover any lost or damaged equipment.

A good suggestion for your students is that they set a timer between observations in order to remember when the next one is due.

The answers to question 7 will vary. Some of the factors related to success will include composition of sucrose solution, temperature, and health and age of the flower head. For question 8, some variability should be noted in terms of pollen tube length. In response to question 9, most pollen tubes will appear similar to an arc of a large circle, as illustrated below.

Shape of typical pollen tube

Dandelion Lab #2:
How Does the Germination Rate of Dandelion Seeds Compare with That of Lettuce Seeds?

SUMMARY. In this lab students collect dandelion "puffballs," remove the seeds, and observe and record the rate of germination. They then do the same with lettuce seeds for comparison. Other environmental factors can be introduced and their effects observed as well.

The main concern in this investigation is that, once moistened, the seeds must not be allowed to dry out. Also, it would be wise to listen to a five-day weather forecast before planning when to collect puffballs. Try for a dry, relatively calm day.

One topic of discussion might be "Why don't all seeds germinate?" Also related would be a long-term investigation into the length of time seeds from a particular plant remain viable and whether refrigeration or freezing lengthens the normal period of viability.

Besides carrying out the suggested investigations that call for altering various environmental factors, you might wish to encourage your students to plant the seedlings or grow the plants—particularly lettuce—hydroponically.

Dandelion Lab #3:
The Effect of Light upon Dandelion Flower Heads

SUMMARY. For this lab students observe the effect of sunlight on the opening and closing of a dandelion flower head. Additional experiments are also suggested for observing this effect. Instructions for collecting *scapes* and for transplanting live plants are both included.

Stress the use of a *young* flower head. The characteristics of a young flower head are mentioned in the Introduction on the student pages. Urge your students to investigate the opening and closing of young flower heads by using complete plants growing in soil.

If your students do use flower heads on scapes, insist that they collect fresh scapes and flower heads every day. Urge them to make the second cut of the scape as soon as possible after cutting it off the plant. When making the second cut, the scape must be cut under the surface of the water. Also, never expose the cut end of the scape to the air! Crushing the region just above the cut is important because this will ensure a continual movement of fluid to the flower head through the fibrovascular bundles in the scape. Adding a very small amount of sugar (just a few granules) will extend the viability of the flower head to some extent. When the scapes are no longer viable, the flower head will close and remain in that state. Flower heads on scapes in water will react to the presence or absence of light only once, possibly twice, before they close up for good.

The answers to the questions will vary.

Dandelion Lab #4:
The Effect of Temperature upon Dandelion Flower Heads

SUMMARY. Students observe the effect of reduced temperature on the opening and closing of dandelion flower heads. Instructions for collecting scapes and for transplanting live plants are both included.

This investigation is very similar to the previous one, which explored the effect of light upon dandelion flower head closure. As stated in the last investigation, using a dandelion plant growing in soil will produce better results than using a flower head on a scape. Point out to your students that the flower head on an isolated scape will most likely open and close only once in response to temperature changes. New scapes must be obtained daily for the investigation to succeed. Again, stress the importance of the second cut being made under water and the addition of a tiny amount of sugar. As the scape tissue dies, the flower head will close up and remain closed in daylight and in warm temperatures.

Earthworm Lab:
How Does Temperature Affect the Pulse Rate of an Earthworm?

SUMMARY. In this lab students examine the anatomy of an earthworm, its "heartbeat," and the effect of lowered temperature on the pulse rate.

This investigation has a number of interesting aspects. For example, if all goes well, the earthworm will be returned alive to its home environment. Making predictions based upon a student-generated graph is another desirable feature.

The main consideration for success is a healthy earthworm. Caution your students regarding the degree of flattening of the earthworm. Only a small amount is necessary, especially if the worm is small and thin.

Results will vary depending upon the vitality of the earthworm and the temperatures involved. Students should neither boil nor freeze the worms. These cautions have been implied rather than explicitly stated in the student pages. If the directions for using warm water as a starting point are followed, then no harm will come to the worm.

Human Behavior Lab #1:
How Does Vision Help Us Maintain
Our Balance?

SUMMARY. In this lab students test the effects of spinning and vision on equilibrium. Students should work together in groups of four to twelve. This investigation can be more fun for students when done with friends, especially ones who are good athletes.

In the first experiment, students should experience increased pressure on the foot on which they are standing. They should also feel constant contractions in the muscles of that leg and foot. These are the minor muscle adjustments that enable them to maintain their balance in this control situation.

The role of vision in helping maintain balance is explored in this second experiment. Students will report that they had greater difficulty in maintaining their balance with their eyes closed than in the control experiment. They should also report that it took longer for them to make adjustments. As a result, they tended to lean farther to the left or to the right than in the control situation. Another observation that should be made is that they had to work harder to maintain their balance, and more muscle effort was involved.

Most students will not be able to maintain their balance after spinning around five times. Those who do will report that they had great difficulty in doing so.

Analysis

1. Spinning interferes with the sense of equilibrium.

2. Our sense of equilibrium plays the greater role in maintaining balance. This is evidenced by the fact that, with eyes closed, it is difficult to maintain our balance. When the sense of equilibrium is negatively affected and both eyes are closed, it is almost impossible to maintain balance.

Human Behavior Lab #2:
What Happens to Our Ability to Taste Sweetness As We Age?

SUMMARY. In this lab students survey individuals in three different age groups to determine whether the ability to taste sweetness varies as people age. Students can perform this investigation individually or in small groups.

This investigation requires some preparation prior to the actual survey of several age groups. Accurate records must be kept and care must be taken in the administration of the sweetener solutions. Although precise instructions are given for preparing the test solutions, slight errors in percentages will not significantly affect the results. When preparing the 0.1% solution, it might be easier to use less than a gram of sweetener and less water (500mL). To do this, a balance will be needed. Since students will be transporting test tubes, plastic test tubes and a test-tube rack should be used to prevent breakage.

Students may experience difficulty getting enough subjects for the older age groups. Another source of possible participants is the school faculty.

The need for keeping subjects free of bias and preconceived ideas as to what taste to expect must be stressed. Also emphasize the need for volunteers to wash out their mouths between tests to avoid carrying over any sweet taste from a previous test.

The sample data sheet is direct and simple. A more elaborate one can be constructed and used, if any youngster desires to do so.

Analysis

1. The plain water acts as a control to ensure that subjects do not report every solution as tasting sweet. The data from any subject who reports that the water tastes sweet should be discarded and another subject's data used.

2. Subjects may say that all the solutions taste sweet in order to please the investigator or because they think it is supposed to be sweet. There are other reasons also.

3. A subject may anticipate and report that the next solution tastes only slightly sweet based on the solutions decreasing in sweetness. The subject might report a sweet taste without really tasting the solution.

4. The larger the sample, the more statistically accurate the results and conclusions.

5. Answers will vary depending upon the subjects used and the strengths of the solutions.

6. More solutions could be used. For example, an investigator might discover that a solution of 0.05% was needed. Another improvement might be to use more groups of people, for example, people in the 20-year-old group. The subjects could all be tested at the same time of day, perhaps 3:00 in the afternoon, which for many people is between lunch and dinner. An assistant could be used to tally the data while the investigator administers the tests.

Human Behavior Lab #3:
What Happens to Our Ability to Taste
Saltiness As We Age?

SUMMARY. This investigation is designed as a follow-up to the investigation on aging and the tasting of sweetness (Human Behavior Lab #2). However, this lab tests the ability to taste salts at different ages. This investigation can be done by students individually or in small groups.

The new concept and procedures are related to the fact that aging appears to affect the tasting of sodium salts differently. Older people will be able to detect some sodium salts in small quantities whereas other salts cannot be detected unless present in fairly substantial amounts. Sodium carbonate is a salt that older people can detect in almost the same concentration that younger people can. On the other hand, sodium sulfate detection requires a concentration 28 times greater than that which can be tasted by a young person. This was reported in a monograph published by the American Dairy Council in April 1990. Your students should be encouraged to use the optional salts, if at all possible.

In this investigation a balance will be necessary to weigh out amounts of the sodium salts.

Analysis

1. Conclusions will vary with the data obtained.

2. a. The results should vary. Low concentrations of sodium chloride, sodium carbonate, and sodium acetate should be detected by the elderly. Sodium sulfate, however, should only be detected in a much higher concentration than the salts just mentioned.

    b. Most likely sodium sulfate.

    c. The order (from most detectable to least) will most likely be: sodium carbonate, sodium chloride, sodium acetate, sodium sulfate.

Human Behavior Lab #4:
What Happens to Our Ability to Taste Sourness As We Age?

SUMMARY. This investigation is designed as a follow-up to Human Behavior Labs #2 and #3. It explores the ability to taste sourness at different ages. This investigation can be done individually or in small groups.

In this investigation students practice a new skill: preparing a number of serial dilutions. The tasting of sour substances was saved for last because there are relatively few taste buds for sourness. Also, they are located on the extreme edges of the tongue and may be difficult for students to touch with the cotton swabs.

A 1mL pipet is included as an optional piece of equipment because these investigations stress common, inexpensive equipment such as a medicine dropper. If the pipet is used, the accuracy of the solutions should be improved and the dilutions could be made more rapidly.

Some interesting data may be forthcoming if the youngsters use the same volunteers for all three taste investigations and do their testing accurately.

You may wish to discuss the evolution of the taste buds in humans if you feel it is appropriate for your students.

Analysis

1. The data using lemon juice will vary depending upon the subjects and the reliability of the diluted solutions as well as many other factors.

2. Conclusions will vary with the data obtained.

3. The results should vary.

4. As the number of elderly people in our population increases, food manufacturers will be challenged to provide products that meet their nutritional and sensory needs, which are different from those of the rest of the population. Older people gradually lose their sense of taste. The older the person, the more likely it is that he or she will have difficulty distinguishing sweet, salty, and sour foods. Older people often complain that food doesn't taste as good as it used to. Chemicals might be added to specially designed foods for the elderly.

5. Our sense of taste serves to warn us that a food may be spoiled or contaminated with a harmful product. For example, a piece of moldy fruit would not taste the

same as a piece of fresh fruit. Thus, our taste buds protect us from becoming ill by eating rotten or spoiled food.

Human Behavior Lab #5:
How Is Your Muscle Strength Affected by Exercise?

> **SUMMARY.** In this lab students use their own arms to test the effect of repetitive exercise on muscle fatigue. Results are charted on a graph by the students. It is recommended that the class work in teams of two.

This investigation requires no sophisticated equipment. The directions are clear and easy to follow. The investigation is generally carried out with enthusiasm if pairs of students are involved. One member of the team is the experimental subject while the other is the timekeeper, counter, and recorder. If this is a class activity, keep the weight uniform by having each student use a copy of the same text or dictionary. The competition factor adds interest and excitement to the discovery of each student's muscle strength.

Conducting a survey of the fatigue factor in arm muscles among all members of a class is a good follow-up. Some students may wish to use family members as experimental subjects. This should be encouraged.

Analysis

1. The points on each student's graph will be unique.

2. The answers will vary. Most graphs will show little loss in the first few exercise sessions.

3. This will vary, but many students will experience the greatest loss around exercise session 7.

4. Conclusions will vary in accordance with the shape of the curve on the graph.

5. The muscles in each arm will probably be similar in terms of loss due to fatigue. However, one arm is usually stronger than the other. People tend to use the stronger arm first.

Human Behavior Lab #6:
How Is Your Muscle Strength Affected
by Temperature?

SUMMARY. This lab requires students to test the effect of cold temperatures on muscle strength and flexibility. The students immerse their hands in ice water and count the number of fists they can make. It is suggested that this experiment be done in pairs—each student can take a turn testing his or her hand while the other assists with counting, etc.

The only piece of scientific equipment needed for this investigation is a thermometer. The rest of the equipment should be available in every school and home.

The main concern is indicated clearly in steps 7 and 8. Although this investigation was field-tested with approximately 100 students in grades seven, eight, and ten, and no students found the cold water to be painful to the point of removal, the caution is included just in case a child does find the cold water painful.

Stress the need for allowing the hand immersed in ice water to return to a near-normal temperature before going on to the next water trial. Also emphasize the importance of having ice floating in the pail of water at all times during the investigation.

Analysis

1. The conclusion of this investigation should be that cold water decreases the ability of the muscles to function.

2. The results for both hands should be similar but not identical.

Human Perspiration Lab:
How Much Perspiration Is Excreted
from One Hand?

SUMMARY. In this lab students observe and record the amount of perspiration secreted from their hands. They then calculate the rate of perspiration per square centimeter of skin on the hand.

This investigation is easy and straightforward. The answers will vary. If you wish, you could have your students include in their calculations the thickness of their hands. Since the thickness of the hand varies from the thumb side to the small finger side, it would be best to have them use a measurement halfway between the two. Then answers will be in cm^3. Emphasize that in the interest of accuracy they should remove as much perspiration as possible from the plastic bag.

Deep-knee bends were suggested because they can be done in the aisle of a regular classroom or a laboratory if the students place their hands on their thighs. Five minutes is the suggested time. More mature students can perform sustained deep-knee bends for longer periods of time. You may wish to increase the time. Consulting your students' physical education teacher would probably be wise if you plan to increase the exercise time period.

Oil Spill Lab #1:
Cleaning Up an Aquatic Oil Spill

SUMMARY. In this lab students simulate an oil spill (using either vegetable or motor oil) and attempt several methods for cleaning it up, including skimming and absorbing the oil.

In the course of carrying out this investigation, students will discover how containment devices work. They will use a variety of materials to clean up a miniature aquatic oil spill. Your students will make judgments concerning the comparative effectiveness of skimming versus absorbing materials for cleaning up oil spills. Finally, students will produce a windstorm to observe the effect of wind and waves upon cleanup efforts.

You should decide whether students will use petroleum or vegetable oil in this investigation. The student pages are written for vegetable oil only.

Petroleum is a complex, thick, dark liquid, composed of many hydrocarbon compounds. Most of the hydrocarbons have chains of 5 to 25 carbon atoms. Motor oil is a fraction petroleum composed of compounds whose chains vary from 15 to 25 carbons. In addition, manufacturers add antioxidants, antivarnish agents, and other additives to their motor oil. Each brand will vary in composition. Another factor that causes variation in motor oil composition is weight, which can vary from 5W to 50W. The heavier the weight, the greater the viscosity of the oil. Additives help determine an oil's viscosity.

Caution your students to pour the oil slowly. When poured slowly, 10W-30 motor oil will remain on the surface of the water. Peanut oil looks very similar to 10W-30 motor oil. It too floats on the surface of the water. Because of the many variables there are no standard answers for the question in 5. Whatever the student observes is the correct answer.

Substituting vegetable oil, a lipid, for motor oil is suggested. Vegetable oil has similar properties to motor oil. Both feel oily and slippery, are insoluble in water, and float. The chief advantage of vegetable oil is that it can be disposed of safely by mixing it with detergent and flushing it into the sewer system.

If motor oil is used, the waste oil should be taken to a garage or auto service station in an appropriate container. Some states mandate that garages must dispose of up to 5 gallons of motor oil in an environmentally safe manner without charge.

Oil Spill Labs #2 and #3:
What Are the Effects of an Aquatic Oil Spill on Seabirds' Feathers? and What Are the Effects of Oil-Soaked Feathers on the Body Temperature of Seabirds?

SUMMARY. In these investigations students simulate the effects of oil spills on seabirds by immersing feathers in oil and observing changes in the drying ability and temperature of the feathers.

The students will make observations of feathers contaminated with oil and make comparisons to water-soaked feathers. The importance of drying feathers that are wet with water and the difficulty involved with drying oil-soaked feathers will become clear. Students should make observations leading to the conclusion that oil-soaked feathers have an adverse effect upon a bird's ability to fly, feed, and swim.

The major safety concern is to prohibit children who are allergic to feathers from participating in this investigation.

Feathers should be supplied for the students. It makes sense to ask the students to contribute an old feather pillow from home, if it is to be discarded. If many feathers are available, a dramatic investigation can illustrate the fact that birds with oil-soaked feathers are in danger of freezing to death. The thermometer in the bag containing the oil-soaked feathers will register lower temperatures sooner than the bag of dry feathers. The temperature change will be rapid.

If motor oil is used, the waste oil should be taken in an appropriate container to a garage or service station for disposal. As mentioned in the previous investigation, many states require automobile repair businesses to get rid of up to 5 gallons of used motor oil brought to them by any person. There is no charge for this service. Vegetable oil can be disposed of safely by mixing it with detergent and water and flushing it directly into the sewer system.

Respiration Lab #1:
How Much Oxygen Do Germinating Seeds Consume in 15 Minutes?

SUMMARY. In this lab students build a respirometer and measure the respiration rate of germinating seeds. This lab is designed to be done along with the other respiration labs. The same respirometer can be used for all the labs. To make meaningful comparisons, the same amount of materials should be introduced into the respirometer in each case.

One important outcome of this investigation is for your students to realize that germinating seeds are alive and use oxygen just as animals do. Another outcome is that students get an opportunity to use manual skills to build the respirometer.

In the interest of safety, it is strongly advised that students use rigid plastic tubing made of polyethylene rather than glass tubing. If you have only glass tubing in your stockroom, then you might want to insert the glass tubing into the stopper for the students. You should also check to be sure that no student carrying on this investigation is allergic to glycerine.

Limewater, which is a saturated solution of calcium hydroxide, will absorb carbon dioxide; however, using it is more time-consuming than using calcium hydroxide paste. The benefit is that limewater is not at all hazardous. If you choose, you can have your students use calcium hydroxide powder in this lab in place of the limewater. Calcium hydroxide, which is far less hazardous than potassium hydroxide (KOH), can irritate the skin, so the students must be advised to wear latex or plastic gloves when handling it. Similarly, students should be cautioned to not inhale the calcium hydroxide powder. Students should fill the test tube up to the 0.5cm mark with the powder. A small amount of water is then added, just enough to make a paste. Waste calcium hydroxide paste can go in the garbage.

Stress the need for the drop of liquid detergent to be close to the opening in the arm of the right angle tube since the movement of the drop will be inward. There will be a wide range of movement of the detergent drop during the timing period. This is due to the many variables involved, such as temperature, moisture content, and health of the germinating seeds.

Questions 1 and 2 have no correct answers due to the numerous variables. The answer is whatever the investigator discovers. For question 3, there should be an increase in the respiration rate with an increase in temperature until the temperature exceeds the viability range for the seeds used in the investigation. Then the respiration rate will start to decrease and eventually stop when the germinating seeds die.

Land Crustacean Lab:
Observing a Living Land Crustacean

SUMMARY. In this lab students examine wood lice or other land crustaceans, induce hypothermia, and look for specific body parts.

For this investigation, any land crustacean in your area will work. Wood lice can be found in damp basements and under logs and rocks. If you can't locate any land crustaceans, sow bugs can be purchased from biological supply houses.

When students observe the wood lice with the hand lens, ask them to determine the number of legs on the thorax and on the abdomen. There will be eight pairs of legs on the wood louse; however, the number of abdominal and thoracic legs will vary depending on the species. The last pair on the abdomen forms the *uropod*, whose function is explained in the procedure. In the introduction, mention is made of air-breathing tracheal tubes. These too vary in number and in position on the legs. Again, variation will be noted from species to species. For example, the common wood louse (*Porcellio scaber*) has tracheae only on the first pair of abdominal limbs, whereas the pill wood louse (*Armadillidium vulgare*) has tracheae on the first five pairs of abdominal legs. The sow bug (*Oniscus asellus*) has no tracheae.

Have your students look for the egg pouch, which will be easy to find. They should also search for the gills, which will be close to where the legs join the body and will be found on the inner side of the limb. When present, the tracheal tube openings (*stigmata*) will be seen on the distal segments of the legs.

Below is a picture of the ventral view of the common wood louse.

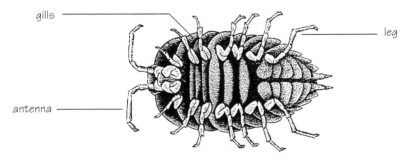

Note: Tracheal openings are found only on the first pair of legs in this species.
The marsupium is not shown in this illustration.

Hypothermia is a good technique for quieting invertebrates. I have used it with success on earthworms and fruit flies (*Drosophila*).

At the end of the investigation, have students return their wood lice to the "home jar." You may wish to keep them for other studies or return them to their natural environment.

Here are answers to questions from the Procedure section:

7. The wood louse requires constant moisture in the form of water droplets. If its gills were to dry up, it would die.

8. The wood louse will roll itself into a ball or "pill."

9. Because of its ability to roll its body into the shape of a pill

10. To conserve moisture

11. *Isopod* refers to the fact that all the legs are similar and none have a special shape, as in the case with the lobster.

Respiration Lab #2:
How Much Oxygen Do Land Crustaceans Consume in 15 Minutes?

SUMMARY. In this lab students measure the respiration rate of land crustaceans (for example, wood lice). This investigation represents a step upward on the evolutionary scale from plants to rather slow-moving invertebrates. More oxygen should be consumed by a gram of land crustaceans than a gram of germinating seeds. This lab can be used as a follow-up to Respiration Lab #1. If so, that lab should be performed before this one is introduced. It is important to use the same respirometer and the same amount of limewater or calcium hydroxide paste for both labs.

In the interest of safety, it is strongly advised that students use rigid plastic tubing made of polyethylene rather than glass tubing. If you have only glass tubing in your stockroom, then you might want to insert the glass tubing into the stopper for the students. You should also check to be sure that no student carrying on this investigation is allergic to glycerine.

Limewater, which is a saturated solution of calcium hydroxide, will absorb carbon dioxide; however, using it is more time-consuming than using calcium hydroxide paste. The benefit is that limewater is not at all hazardous. If you choose, you can have your students use calcium hydroxide powder in this lab in place of the limewater. Calcium hydroxide, which is far less hazardous than potassium hydroxide (KOH), can irritate the skin, so the students must be advised to wear latex or plastic gloves when handling it. Similarly, students should be cautioned to not inhale the calcium hydroxide powder. Students should fill the test tube up to the 0.5cm mark with the powder. A small amount of water is then added, just enough to make a paste. Waste calcium hydroxide paste can go in the garbage.

Analysis

1. As the temperature increases, there should also be an increase in the respiration rate. When the temperature becomes too high for an organism to survive, the respiration rate will decrease and, upon death, reach zero.

2. Time of day should not be a factor. Relative humidity would be a factor because of the wood louse's need for keeping its gills moist. (An investigation into the relation between the respiration rate of land crustaceans and relative humidity could be undertaken by a motivated, capable student.)

Respiration Lab #3:
How Much Oxygen Do Adult House Crickets Consume in 15 Minutes?

SUMMARY. In this lab students measure the respiration rate of adult house crickets. This lab is designed as a follow-up to Respiration Labs #2 and #3. Those labs should be performed before this one is done. It is important to use the same respirometer and the same amount of limewater or calcium hydroxide paste for all labs.

This investigation and Respiration Lab #4 afford your students the opportunity to study the life cycle of the house cricket. In addition, students may become fascinated by this organism to the extent of wanting to make one of them a pet. Many biological supply houses sell cages as well as crickets. It is essential to obtain parental approval before ordering a cricket cage and crickets for your students to take home.

Since house crickets are inexpensive, it would be wiser to purchase them from a biological supply company rather than trying to collect them on your own. However, there is nothing wrong with having your students collect field crickets if your school is located near meadows and fields and if the collection is not carried out in the winter. Field crickets spend the winter as nymphs in burrows which are about 30 cm underground. The cost of house crickets, at this writing, was less than $5.00 for a dozen. After this investigation is completed, the crickets could be added to the school's collection of living organisms or taken home to be pets.

In the interest of safety, it is strongly advised that students use rigid plastic tubing made of polyethylene rather than glass tubing. If you have only glass tubing in your stockroom, then you might want to insert the glass tubing into the stopper for the students. You should also check to be sure that no student carrying on this investigation is allergic to glycerine.

Limewater, which is a saturated solution of calcium hydroxide, will absorb carbon dioxide; however, using it is more time-consuming than using calcium hydroxide paste. The benefit is that limewater is not at all hazardous. If you choose, you can have your students use calcium hydroxide powder in this lab in place of the limewater. Calcium hydroxide, which is far less hazardous than potassium hydroxide (KOH), can irritate the skin, so the students must be advised to wear latex or plastic gloves when handling it. Similarly, students should be cautioned to not inhale the calcium hydroxide powder. Students should fill the test tube up to the 0.5cm mark with the powder. A small amount of water is then added, just enough to make a paste. Waste calcium hydroxide paste can go in the garbage.

Analysis

1. Both males and females should use the same amount of oxygen under usual and normal conditions.

2. As the temperature of the environment decreases, so will the respiration rate.

Respiration Lab #4:
How Much Oxygen Do House Cricket Nymphs Consume in 15 Minutes?

> **SUMMARY.** In this lab students measure the respiration rate of house cricket nymphs, using a respirometer. This lab is designed to be a follow-up to Respiration Labs #1 through #3. Those labs should be done prior to this one. Be sure to use the same respirometer and the same amount of limewater or calcium hydroxide paste for all labs.

This investigation presents an excellent opportunity for your students to study the life cycle of the house cricket from nymph to adult. Purchasing the nymphs from a biological supply company is far easier and more efficient than trying to capture house crickets in a nymph stage. The nymphs could be added to your school's collection and allowed to grow to adulthood after this investigation is completed.

In the interest of safety, it is strongly advised that students use rigid plastic tubing made of polyethylene rather than glass tubing. If you have only glass tubing in your stockroom, then you might want to insert the glass tubing into the stopper for the students. You should also check to be sure that no student carrying on this investigation is allergic to glycerine.

Limewater, which is a saturated solution of calcium hydroxide, will absorb carbon dioxide; however, using it is more time-consuming than using calcium hydroxide paste. The benefit is that limewater is not at all hazardous. If you choose, you can have your students use calcium hydroxide powder in this lab in place of the limewater. Calcium hydroxide, which is far less hazardous than potassium hydroxide (KOH), can irritate the skin, so the students must be advised to wear latex or plastic gloves when handling it. Similarly, students should be cautioned to not inhale the calcium hydroxide powder. Students should fill the test tube up to the 0.5cm mark with the powder. A small amount of water is then added, just enough to make a paste. Waste calcium hydroxide paste can go in the garbage.

Analysis

1. The respiration rate of the nymphs should be lower at the lower temperature. Thus, their respiration rate will be highest at a time of day when the temperature is the hottest.

Seedling Power Lab:
How Powerful Are Emerging Seedlings?

> **SUMMARY.** In this lab students test the strength of sprouting seedlings and determine whether the seeds can break through a variety of surfaces.

This investigation is clear and straightforward. The sand mix—which is really cement—is optional because it is harder to work with than plaster of paris or spackling paste.

Make sure that the students water their containers thoroughly before applying the covering material. Urge them to be as accurate as possible when applying the covering material. They should try not to put in too much or too little.

Timing is the most important consideration. Planting should be done on a Friday before a week in which there are no school holidays. This will allow for a two-day growth period (Saturday and Sunday) and five consecutive days for observation. You should decide how many covering materials your students can apply in one laboratory session. If your class has a double- or triple-period lab, all the setting up could be done in one day. If you have only a single lab period, then you should do this investigation in sections rather than rushing to complete it in one period.

The extra cups can be used for mixing or to replace any labeled cups that break when being filled or covered.

Analysis

1–3. Plaster of paris—Most seeds of all types should penetrate the 0.5cm thickness. Fewer will break through the 1.0cm layer and still fewer emerge through the 1.5cm layer.

4–6. Spackling paste—The results should be similar to those observed with the plaster of paris.

7–9. Sand mix—The results will vary depending on how accurately the students measured the amounts of mix and water. In general, few or no seeds should break up the sand mix cover. The thicker the cover, the less penetration by the seedlings.

10. The corn will probably show the most root growth.

11. The lettuce should show the least root growth.

12. The results for the grass seed and the lettuce should be similar. The results for the corn and the pea should be similar. The breaking up of a particular covering material is dependent on the thickness of the seedling stem rather than on whether a plant is a dicot or monocot.

13. More corn and pea seedlings should penetrate the covering layers than grass and lettuce seedlings. The seedling's stem diameter is the key factor. Usually a large seed will produce a seedling with a relatively thick stem.

Spider Lab #1:
How Are Spiders Different from Insects?

SUMMARY. Students examine the anatomy of preserved spiders and compare it with that of insects. They compare the spider with the cricket studied in Respiration Lab #3. Alternatively, they can compare the spider with a cricket during this lab.

Perhaps due to an acquired, irrational fear, spiders are never found in laboratory manuals for secondary school youngsters. This investigation primarily focuses on the external anatomy of preserved spiders. A second aim is to have the students compare spiders with insects. Ideally you should stress the beneficial aspects of spiders: that they are carnivores that feed mainly on insects.

The main safety consideration is the avoidance of the black widow spider. The chance of coming across one is very slight, but it is possible and that is why caution is stressed.

Observations

1. The second pair of appendages are called *pedipalps*. They are similar to the walking legs but are shorter and are similar to a *palpus* (a sensory segmented mouth part). Insects have antennae as the first pair of appendages.

2. The openings of the poison glands are tiny holes near the tip of the *chelicerae*. The chelicerae are composed of two joints: a basal portion and an opposable claw. The appearance will vary, depending upon the species of spider that is being examined.

3. Some spiders cover their prey with enzymes secreted by the digestive tract before chewing it. Others pump enzymes onto the prey; digestion takes place externally, and the spider swallows the "nutritive soup."

4. Generally spiders have eight simple eyes arranged in two rows, but they have trouble seeing. Some spiders have only six eyes. The body and legs have sensory hairs on them that provide the spider with information about its environment.

5. The posterior section resembles a bag and is larger than the anterior section.

6. The third pair of appendages are very similar to the walking legs.

7. There are four pairs of walking legs.

8. The *spinnerets* are tiny fingerlike organs located on the ventral side near the rear of the abdomen, just below the anus. There are three pairs of spinnerets. The *book lungs* are a series of air-filled sacs that hang in leaflike folds of the body wall. They look like the pages of a book.

Analysis

1. Spiders spin webs to trap insects. They have poison glands to kill their prey.

2. Spiders have eight walking legs whereas insects have six. Insects use *spiracles* for breathing whereas spiders have book lungs. Spiders are carnivores whereas insects feed on many kinds of food. The first appendages of spiders are the clawlike chelicerae whereas insects have antennae. Spiders have sensory hairs and insects do not. Spiders have eight simple eyes and insects have two large compound eyes.

Spider Lab #2:
How Do Spider Webs Trap Insects?

SUMMARY. This lab can't be done in class, but it could be used as a homework assignment for all students, as a makeup activity for those who have missed previous work, or as an extra-credit project.

Several common misconceptions are clarified in this investigation: first, the idea that all spiders spin webs; second, that all parts of the spider's web are sticky; third, that all spiders stay in their web. Another expected outcome is an appreciation for the engineering ability of spiders.

1. The mapmaking activity can be best carried out using an orb web.

2. The dimensions of spider webs will vary.

3. Answers will vary.

4. The appearance of the spider will vary.

5. Sketches will vary but should be similar to the kind of web a child sees.

6. The upper edge thread is at the top of the orb web.

7. The center threads form the smallest circles and are in the center of the web.

8. The radial threads run from the center to the periphery of the web.

9. The sticky threads extend outward from the center threads to the edge threads that form the last circle. Safe threads include the center threads, radial threads, and edge threads.

10. The cotton swab should tend to stick to the tiny adhesive drop.

11. There will be a wide variation in answers.

Analysis

1. Both are made of silk spun by spiders. Both may have insects trapped in them. Spiders might be present or absent in both cases.

2. Sticky threads should be present in the orb but not in the sheet web. General size and appearance of the webs should be different.

3. Spiders use silk to spin the cocoons in which their eggs develop and to construct webs and "lifelines."

Vinegar Eel Lab #1:
Are Vinegar Eels Attracted to Light?

SUMMARY. In this lab students test the reaction of vinegar eels to light stimulus. They will use test tubes in different configurations for this observation. This lab is designed to be followed by Vinegar Eel Lab #2.

Vinegar eels are a rarity in the class of roundworms because they are nonparasitic. This, coupled with their hardiness, make them ideal experimental organisms for embryonic biologists to use for investigative purposes. They can be purchased from most biological supply companies. You can buy all you will initially need for less than $5.00. Then, since these organisms are hardy and reproduce readily, you can breed the amount you need for experimental purposes.

Analysis

1. With your students, review the following possibilities:

    a. If vinegar eels are attracted to light, they should be scattered throughout Test Tube #2 and congregated at the window in Test Tube #3.

    b. If light is not the stimulus that causes the eels to gather at the surface of their culture medium, they will be found at or near the surface of all three test tubes.

Vinegar Eel Lab #2:
Do Vinegar Eels Respond Negatively to Gravity?

> **SUMMARY.** In this follow-up to Vinegar Eel Lab #1, students test the eels' response to gravity by observing their behavior in tubes with a variety of orientations.

Clear plastic tubing is available from pet shops that sell aquarium supplies, from hardware stores, and from scientific supply companies. Tubing clamps or rubber bands can be used to seal the ends of the tubing pieces. The reason for excluding as much air as possible from each piece of tubing is to eliminate another possibility: that vinegar eels may gather at the surface because of their need for oxygen. This is very plausible, but difficult to test when one is on a low budget, using simple equipment. Have your students make every effort to remove all the air from the pieces of tubing before sealing them.

Stress the need for making prompt observations once the black covering is removed form the circular tubes.

Analysis

1. With your students, review the following possibilities:

a. If negative *geotaxis* is the reason why the vinegar eels collect at the surface, they should be found at the top of all three circular tubes despite the fact that the three circles are aligned in different spatial planes.

b. If negative geotaxis is not the reason for their behavior, the eels should be dispersed throughout each circle when observed—provided there was no air in any of the tubing.

Dandelion Lab #1

Inducing and Observing the Growth of Pollen Tubes from Dandelion Pollen Grains

Introduction

Pollen tubes are found in flowering (*angiosperm*) plants, and their function is to deliver the *sperm nuclei* to the *ovules*. In this lab you are going to stimulate the pollen grains of the dandelion to grow pollen tubes by placing the grains in a 5% sugar solution. Growth may begin as early as 30 minutes after the pollen grains are put in the growth medium, or it may not start until 90 minutes or longer have passed. To save time, your teacher may have started stimulating pollen grain growth before you entered the laboratory.

Materials

- Several dandelions with healthy, young, yellow flower heads
- Microscope slides
- Microscope or 2 hand lenses (6X)
- Sucrose (white table sugar)
- Graduated cylinder
- Lens tissue
- Water
- Weighing paper
- Watch or clock
- Medicine dropper
- Balance scale
- Spatula
- Transparent metric ruler

Procedure

1. Use the spatula to transfer sugar from container to balance scale. Prepare a 5% solution of sucrose (white table sugar) by dissolving 2.5g of sugar in 43mL of water. The percentage is not critical and the solution will work in a range between 4% and 8%. You can even estimate the amounts if you don't have a balance scale and a graduated cylinder.

2. Hold a dandelion *scape* (stalk) with your thumb and first two fingers so that the flower head is firmly secured. Tap the flower head gently over the center of a microscope slide that has been cleaned. You should be able to see a fine dust of yellow pollen. If you don't, repeat the tapping using different flower heads. Continue using different flower heads until you do see some pollen grains on the slide.

(continued)

Name _____ Date _____

Inducing and Observing the Growth of Pollen Tubes from Dandelion Pollen Grains
(continued)

3. When pollen grains become visible, place a drop of the sugar solution on top of them. Using the low-power objective of the microscope, check to be sure that the pollen grains are in the drop of sugar solution. If a microscope is not available, you can use two similar hand lenses held on top of each other, as in the diagram that follows. Looking through the pair will approximately double the magnification.

Two magnifying lenses held together

In the space provided below, draw several dandelion pollen grains as you see them under magnification.

Fill in the data table below.

Time began _____	**Time pollen tube growth was first noted** _____

(continued)

Dandelion Lab #1

Inducing and Observing the Growth of Pollen Tubes from Dandelion Pollen Grains
(continued)

4. When the pollen tubes first start to grow, they look like little bumps on the pollen grains. This diagram gives you a good idea of what to look for.

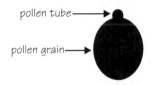

5. Scan your slide every 30 minutes to look for pollen tubes growing. When you find one or more growing, keep your microscope focused over them. **Don't let the pollen grains dry up.** Replenish the sugar solution from time to time by adding a drop or two of the sugar solution.

6. After growth has begun, make observations every 30 minutes. Record these observations by making detailed drawings in the spaces below.

30 minutes after initial growth	60 minutes after initial growth	90 minutes after initial growth

(continued)

Dandelion Lab #1

Inducing and Observing the Growth of Pollen Tubes from Dandelion Pollen Grains
(continued)

7. Make a rough estimate of the number of pollen grains that germinated: _____
   What is the approximate number of pollen grains on the slide? _____ What is
   the approximate percentage of pollen grains that grew pollen tubes? _____%
   What is a possible explanation for this percentage? _____
   _____
   _____

8. Are all the pollen tubes identical in length? _____
   By mounting a transparent metric ruler on the microscope stage parallel to the
   slide, you can make a rough estimate of the length of the pollen tubes in *microme-*
   ters (1,000 micrometers = 1 millimeter). What is the length, in micrometers, of the
   shortest pollen tube? _____ the longest pollen tube? _____

9. Are all the pollen tubes the same shape, or do the shapes vary? _____
   In the space below, draw a typical pollen tube and then draw the one you think is
   the most unusual.

Typical	Unusual

Name _____   Date _____

How Does the Germination Rate of Dandelion Seeds Compare with That of Lettuce Seeds?

Introduction

To most people, dandelions are weeds. By definition a weed is an unwanted plant. In this investigation, you will be given a basic technique for germinating dandelion seeds, each of which is enclosed in its own fruit. The same technique can also be used for germinating lettuce seeds. (Lettuce is not a weed since it is a desirable crop.) After completing the basic investigation, you can vary environmental conditions to see how hardy dandelion seeds (or any other seeds) are and under what conditions they germinate well or poorly. Naturally, a *control* must be used as part of each investigation into the factors affecting seeds (in this case the control will be lettuce seeds). A minimum of 20 seeds should be used in each case. The larger the number of seeds used, the more accurate your results will be. Collect dandelion puffballs by placing a plastic bag over the ball and cutting the scape. Seal the plastic bag to prevent loss of the fruits (or seeds). Locking plastic bags are the most convenient type to use. It is best to collect dandelion fruit when the weather is dry and the winds relatively calm.

Materials

- Plastic bags (locking type, if possible, and large enough to seal one of the plates inside)
- Paper towels
- Magnifying lens
- Glass or beaker with water
- Single-edged razor blade or nail clipper
- Lettuce seeds (any variety)
- Dandelion in the puff-ball state
- Forceps
- Transparent tape
- Masking tape
- Marking pen or pencil
- Small plates (2)
- Medicine dropper

(continued)

Dandelion Lab #2

How Does the Germination Rate of Dandelion Seeds Compare with That of Lettuce Seeds?
(continued)

Procedure

1. Using the forceps, remove 20 fruits from the dandelion puffball. The fruit is the small brown structure under the parachute. There are usually 60 or more on an intact head. Each is attached to the parachute by a long thread or stem. The other end is attached to the flower head of the dandelion. Each fruit contains a single seed.

2. Remove each fruit from its parachute by holding the stem that attaches the fruit to its parachute with your forceps. Use a nail clipper to cut off the attaching stem, allowing the fruit to fall into one of the small plates. A single-edged razor blade or scalpel can also be used. Discard the stem and parachute.

3. Thoroughly moisten a paper towel, using the water in the beaker. Be sure the towel is wet but not dripping. In order to germinate, water will be absorbed by the seeds and used by the emerging plants. During the course of your investigation, check every day or two to be sure the towel is moist. When necessary, add water in small quantities using a medicine dropper.

4. Lay the towel so that half of it is on a plate. Place the 20 dandelion fruits (seeds) on the wet towel. Arrange them in four rows of five fruits (seeds) per row.

5. Now fold the other half of the wet towel over the seeds so that there is wet paper beneath them and on top of them. Place the plate inside one of the plastic bags. Seal the bag. If it isn't a bag of the locking type, seal it with transparent tape.

6. Use a marking pen or pencil to identify these seeds. Label "Experimental Seed" directly on the outside of the plastic bag or on a piece of masking tape.

7. Using lettuce seeds, repeat steps 3 through 5. Try to keep the environmental conditions identical for both groups of seeds.

8. Use a marking pencil or pen to identify these seeds. Label them "Control Seed."

9. For ten days check both sets of seeds daily for germination. Keep accurate records in a data table similar to the one below. When a seed germinates, remove it from the wet towel. Don't forget to record it as "germinated" in the data table.

(continued)

Name _____   Date _____

How Does the Germination Rate of Dandelion Seeds Compare with That of Lettuce Seeds?
(continued)

MODEL DATA TABLE										
	Number of Seeds Germinated									
	Day 1	**Day 2**	**Day 3**	**Day 4**	**Day 5**	**Day 6**	**Day 7**	**Day 8**	**Day 9**	**Day 10**
Lettuce	0	4	7	7	1	0	0	0	0	0
Dandelion	0	1	0	10	1	0	1	0	0	0

Note: Not all seeds germinated. This is to be expected. Many factors such as age affect the percentage of seeds that germinate. The germination rate for the lettuce seeds was 95%. In the case of the 20 dandelion seeds, the rate was only 65%.

Here are some environmental factors to investigate to determine whether they affect the germination rate of seeds:

1. Exposure to light of different wavelengths (different-colored lights)

2. Exposure to magnetic fields

3. Exposure to electromagnetic fields

4. Chemical additives to the water (vitamins, aspirin, antibiotics)

5. Different temperatures (use the refrigerator for cool temperatures)

Use the following table with the environmental factors:

	Number of Seeds Germinated									
	Day 1	**Day 2**	**Day 3**	**Day 4**	**Day 5**	**Day 6**	**Day 7**	**Day 8**	**Day 9**	**Day 10**
Environmental Factor										
Control										

Name _____ Date _____

Dandelion Lab #3

The Effect of Light upon Dandelion Flower Heads

Introduction

Young dandelion flowers react to the presence and absence of light. In the absence of light, young dandelion flower heads will close. In their normal environment, the heads will close after sundown; during the daylight hours, the flower heads will be open. The flower heads will continue to open and close until all the florets in the flower head have bloomed. The response to light can be observed only in young dandelion flower heads. If you remove a flower head and its scape, the closing action can be observed for approximately one day (24 hours), provided the scape is kept in water. Unfortunately, only partial closing of the flower head will occur when it and its scape are snipped off the parent plant. Also, more time will be required for closing as compared to a similar flower head on a growing plant. Thus, this phenomenon is best observed and researched in a living, growing plant.

You could use a dandelion plant in its natural habitat, or you could transplant a dandelion plant to a flower pot and carry out this investigation at home or in school. If growing a complete dandelion plant in school or at home presents problems, then use healthy young flower heads and their scapes for your investigations into the effect light has upon dandelion flower heads. Directions for each option follow.

Transplanting a Dandelion Plant to a Flower Pot

1. First you will remove as much of the plant, especially its roots and the surrounding soil, as possible. Use a trowel or knife to remove the entire plant including leaves, stems, and roots. Dig or cut a circle of soil around the plant (the center of the circle). The radius of the circle should be 12–15cm (the diameter of the circle will be 24–30cm). Dig down to a depth of 10cm or more. The object is to keep intact as much of the root structure as possible.

2. Next you will transplant the dandelion plant and its accompanying soil into a flower pot that has a drainage hole in the bottom. Be sure the pot is large enough to accommodate the plant as well as some additional potting soil under and around the transplanted dandelion. First place some potting soil in the bottom of the pot. Now place the dandelion in the center of the pot. Add potting soil around the transplant. Tamp down the soil with your fingers. Add enough soil so the top of the soil is level with the top of the plant.

(continued)

8   *25 Low-Cost Biology Investigations*

Dandelion Lab #3

The Effect of Light upon Dandelion Flower Heads (*continued*)

3. Water the plant daily for a week. By then new roots will have formed and the dandelion will be ready for use as a research tool.

Preparing Scapes for Light Experiments

Use new scapes and flower heads daily.

1. You will need a wide-mouth jar containing a minimum of 8cm of water, a small pair of scissors, and a small amount of granular sugar.

2. With the scissors, snip off a scape that bears a young flower head near its base. A young flower head has bright yellow, erect florets and is completely open.

3. Now submerge the cut end in the water. **Keeping the cut end under water, cut off 1cm or so of the scape**. Make the cut at an angle. (See the diagram below.) Using your thumb and forefinger, gently crush the scape in the region just above the diagonal cut. The reason this second cut is made under water and the scape tissue is crushed near the cut is to eliminate air bubbles that could block the water transportation tubes in the scape. If the tubes were blocked, the flower head would soon die and no reaction to light would occur.

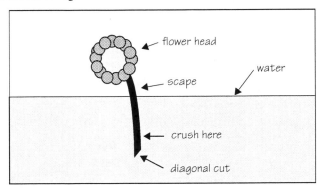

4. Add 8–10 grains of sugar to the water. The added sugar will increase the reaction time of the flower head. **Adding too much sugar will do more harm than good.**

(continued)

Name _____ Date _____

The Effect of Light upon Dandelion
Flower Heads (*continued*)

Materials

- Dandelion flower head (either on an intact plant or on a scape in water)
- Dandelion plant
- Light-proof enclosure (box, black plastic bag, etc.)

Procedure

1. Observe a young dandelion flower head either on a healthy growing plant (in the schoolyard or in a vacant lot) or in a jar. Look for a bright yellow flower head that is wide open. Cover the plant or jar with a box, black plastic bag, or anything that will prevent the light from reaching the flower head. Be sure the light-proof enclosure makes good contact with the ground or tabletop so that no light will reach the flower or the plant.

   After ten minutes, remove the light-proof cover and observe the flower head. Has the flower head started to close? _____ Replace the light-proof cover and continue to observe at five-minute intervals.

   How long did it take before you first noticed the flower head starting to close? _____ How long did it take for the flower head to close completely? _____

2. After the flower head is completely closed, remove the light-proof enclosure. How long does it take for the flower head to open completely? _____ How does this time compare with the closing time? _____

_____

(continued)

Name _____   Date _____

The Effect of Light upon Dandelion
Flower Heads (*continued*)

The opening and closing of the flower head in response to the presence or absence of sunlight represent a basic experiment or starting point. There are any number of additional investigations you can do, for example:

1. How many times can you cause a dandelion flower head to open and close during three hours of daylight? Does the time for this response remain the same over the three hours? Prepare a bar or line graph to show your results.

2. Using different-colored plastic wraps as light filters, determine which color light, if any, will cause the dandelion flower head to close.

Color	Approximate Wavelength
blue	450nm
green	525nm
yellow	600nm
red	660nm

3. Do dandelion flower heads, placed in a dark room after the sun has gone down, open if they are exposed to artificial light? If so, determine the minimum amount of light necessary to produce opening. Use a variety of light bulbs that produce different amounts of illumination (40 watts, 60 watts, 75 watts, etc.). Keep the distance between the dandelion and the bulb the same for each bulb. Record and graph the time it took each bulb to open the flower head. Is there a relationship between the number of watts and the time required for dandelion flower heads to open?

4. Place a dandelion flower head in a dark room after sundown, add a light with constant watts (100 watts), and vary the distance between the flower head and the light source. Start with 10cm, then 20cm, 40cm, and finally 80cm. Graph your results. What are your conclusions?

Dandelion Lab #4

The Effect of Temperature Upon Dandelion Flower Heads

Introduction

Dandelion flower heads open and close in response to temperature changes. The flower heads close when the temperature drops. In this investigation you will attempt to determine how many degrees the temperature must fall in order for the flower heads to close during daylight hours. As is the case with their response to the absence of light, flower heads will continue to open and close until all the flowers have bloomed. Since this can best be observed in the growing dandelion plant, it is best to use a potted plant as the experimental subject.

If growing a complete dandelion plant in school or at home presents problems, then use healthy young flower heads and their scapes for your investigations of temperature's effect upon dandelion flower heads.

Directions for each option follow.

Transplanting a Dandelion Plant to a Flower Pot

1. First you will remove as much of the plant, especially its roots and the surrounding soil, as possible. Use a trowel or knife to remove the entire plant including leaves, stems, and roots. Dig or cut a circle of soil around the plant (the center of the circle). The radius of the circle should be 12–15cm (the diameter of the circle will be 24–30cm). Dig down to a depth of 10cm or more. The object is to keep intact as much of the root structure as possible.

2. Next you will transplant the dandelion plant and its accompanying soil into a flower pot that has a drainage hole in the bottom. Be sure the pot is large enough to accommodate the plant as well as some additional potting soil under and around the transplanted dandelion. First place some potting soil in the bottom of the pot. Now place the dandelion in the center of the pot. Add potting soil around the transplant. Tamp down the soil with your fingers. Add enough soil so the top of the soil is level with the top of the plant.

(continued)

Dandelion Lab #4

The Effect of Temperature upon Dandelion
Flower Heads (continued)

3. Water the plant daily for a week. By then new roots will have formed and the dandelion will be ready for use as a research tool.

Preparing Scapes for Temperature Experiments

Use new scapes and flower heads daily.

1. You will need a wide-mouth jar containing a minimum of 8cm of water, a small pair of scissors, and a small amount of granular sugar.

2. With the scissors, snip off a scape that bears a young flower head near its base. A young flower head has bright yellow, erect florets and is completely open.

3. Now submerge the cut end in the water. **Keeping the cut end under water, cut off 1cm or so of the scape**. Make the cut at an angle. (See the diagram below.) Using your thumb and forefinger, gently crush the scape in the region just above the diagonal cut. The reason this second cut is made under water and the scape tissue is crushed near the cut is to eliminate air bubbles that could block the water transportation tubes in the scape. If the tubes were blocked, the flower head would soon die and no reaction would occur.

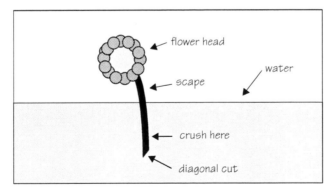

4. Add 8–10 grains of sugar to the water. The added sugar will increase the reaction time of the flower head. **Adding too much sugar will do more harm than good.**

(continued)

Name _____ Date _____

The Effect of Temperature upon Dandelion Flower Heads (*continued*)

Materials

- Dandelion flower head (on an intact plant or on a dissected scape)
- Ice cubes
- Battery jar (wide enough and tall enough to hold the dandelion plant or scape)
- Thermometer
- Transparent tape
- Piece of plastic wrap (wide enough to cover the top of the battery jar)

Procedure

1. Place an open dandelion flower head (either a dandelion plant in a flower pot or a scape in a small jar with water) in the center of the battery jar. Do this during the daylight hours to eliminate the absence of light as a variable. Record the air temperature in the data table on page 15.

2. Remove the dandelion plant and its container from the battery jar. Place a single layer of ice cubes on the bottom of the battery jar. Replace the dandelion plant. (Avoid direct contact with the dandelion plant or scape.) You want to cool the air in the battery jar, not freeze the plant itself.

3. Cover the top of the battery jar with the plastic wrap. Seal it with transparent tape.

4. For every drop of 4°C observe the amount of dandelion flower closure. Record the temperatures and amounts of closure in the data table. Stop when the flower head is completely closed or when the air temperature reaches 10°C.

(continued)

Name _____ Date _____

The Effect of Temperature upon Dandelion Flower Heads (continued)

DATA TABLE	
Temperature	**Amount of Closure (None, Half, Complete)**
Air temperature:	
-4°:	
-4°:	
-4°:	
-4°:	

5. At what temperature did closure of the flower head start? _____

   _____

   _____

6. How long did it take for closure of the flower head to be completed? _____

   _____

   _____

Name _____ Date _____

Earthworm Lab

How Does Temperature Affect the Pulse Rate of an Earthworm?

Introduction

Earthworms are useful soil-dwelling creatures that can fertilize and aerate about 200g of earth in a single day. These creatures lack lungs but use their thin skin to absorb atmospheric gases and water. These materials enter their blood vessels which lie close to the moist, thin skin. Changes in temperature will be quickly transferred to the blood inside the blood vessels. If the earthworm is flattened and a strong light is used, it is possible to see the *aortic arches*, which are the equivalent of hearts. They pulsate as they pump blood throughout the earthworm's body. This information is the basis of this investigation.

Materials

- Live, healthy earthworm (12-15cm in length)
- Jar containing moist soil or grass
- Paper towels
- Standing lamp (100-watt bulb or stronger)
- Ice cubes
- Thermometer
- Toothpicks
- Water (warm)
- 20cm glass squares (2)
- Deep aluminum pan
- Petroleum jelly
- Forceps

Procedure

1. Moisten one of the glass squares with water. Place the worm on the moistened square. If you use forceps to handle the worm, be careful that you don't injure the creature.

2. Put a blob of petroleum jelly at each corner of the second glass square. Base the amount on the fact that you are going to sandwich the worm between the glass squares.

3. Once your "worm sandwich" is made, gently squeeze the two plates together until the worm is *slightly* flattened. If you flatten the worm too much, it will die; there should be a little room for the worm to move around.

(continued)

Earthworm Lab

How Does Temperature Affect the Pulse Rate
of an Earthworm? (*continued*)

4. Turn on the lamp and hold your worm sandwich up so that the light is coming from behind it. You should be able to see the pulsating aortic arches and larger blood vessels. You may be able to see as many as ten aortic arches.

5. Using the thermometer, record the air temperature. Then count the pulsations per minute of the earthworm's aortic arches or large blood vessels. Record this data in the table on the following page.

6. Add warm water to the aluminum pan. Use water that is between 25° and 30°C. Record the temperature of the water in the data table.

7. Place the glass sandwich *vertically* into the water, making sure that the front half of the earthworm is not submerged. After five minutes, remove the glass sandwich. Count the number of heartbeats (pulsations per minute) and record the amount in the data table.

8. Add a few ice cubes to the water. When the temperature of the water in the pan has decreased approximately 5°C, return the earthworm sandwich to the water as you did in step 7. Wait five minutes, remove the worm, and count the number of pulsations per minute. Record the number in the data table.

9. Add more ice cubes. When the water temperature has gone down another 5°C, return the worm sandwich to the water for another five minutes. Don't use water that is below 10°C. Record the number of pulsations per minute in the data table.

10. If time permits, remove the ice cubes and reverse the investigation. Do this by adding small amounts of hot water to cold water. When you reach each of the temperatures previously recorded in your data table, determine the number of pulsations per minute.

    Are your results the same as those you obtained when cooling the water? _____

    _____ If your results are *not* the same, how can you explain the differences?

    _____

    _____

    _____

(continued)

Earthworm Lab

How Does Temperature Affect the Pulse Rate of an Earthworm? (*continued*)

1. Return the earthworm to its jar of moist grass or soil. Later, return the worm, which should be in relatively good condition, to its normal environment (your garden or lawn).

DATA TABLE			
Air temperature:		°C	Pulsations per minute:
Initial water temperature:		°C	Pulsations per minute:
Cooler water temperature:		°C	Pulsations per minute:
Colder water temperature:		°C	Pulsations per minute:

Conclusions

1. Whatistheeffectoftemperatureuponthenumberofpulsationsperminuteoftheearthworm?

   _____

2. Graph your results below. Predict the number of pulsations per minute that will occur at both 30°C and 5°C: 30°C _____ 5°C _____

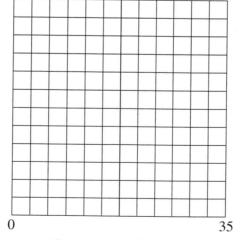

Number of pulsations per minute

0   35

Temperature in degrees C

   25 Low-Cost Biology Investigations

Name _____   Date _____

How Does Vision Help Us Maintain Our Balance?

Introduction

Our ability to maintain our balance depends upon equilibrium that we sense through organs in our inner ears. One set of organs, the *semicircular canals*, make us aware of circular motion. The *vestibular sacs* allow us to sense our position and sense motion in a straight line. When we get sensory clues that we are losing our balance, we make compensatory (neutralizing) muscular adjustments that return us to a balanced state. These adjustments are so automatic and small that we often fail to appreciate their importance. You will investigate the role of these adjustments, and the role that vision and your eyes play in maintaining balance.

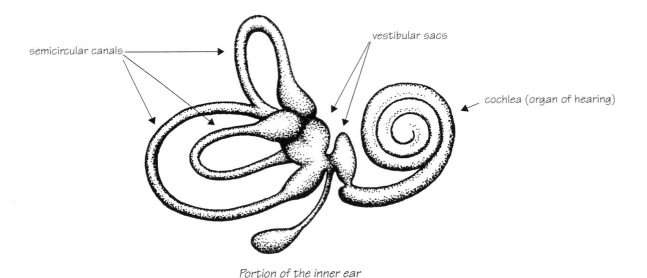

Portion of the inner ear

Materials

| • Pencil or pen | • Paper | • Clock or watch |

(continued)

Human Behavior Lab #1

How Does Vision Help Us Maintain
Our Balance? (continued)

Procedure

1. This part of the investigation will be the control. Appoint one person to be the timekeeper. Everyone else is to stand on one foot for 30 seconds without holding onto anything. While doing so, you should make a mental note of the sensations experienced in that leg and foot. After the 30 seconds record these sensations on a piece of paper. This data should be written under the heading "Control Situation— Eyes Open." As a group, discuss what sensations you experienced. If any sensations mentioned by group members are ones that you experienced but forgot, add them to your list.

2. After a brief rest, repeat the first procedure—that is, stand on one foot for 30 seconds. This time, close both eyes as you lift one foot off the ground. Once again, make a mental note of the sensations experienced. Also, compare these sensations to those experienced previously. Record these observations in written form and compare them with the first set. Do this under the heading "Balancing with Eyes Closed." As a group, discuss what sensations you experienced. If any sensations mentioned are ones experienced but forgotten, add them to your list.

3. After another brief rest, carry out the final phase of this investigation. With both eyes open, spin around *quickly* in a tight circle five times. Immediately shut your eyes and attempt to stand on one foot for 30 seconds, as was done before. Note the sensations. Write these observations under the heading "Balancing with Eyes Closed and Equilibrium Disrupted." Compare these sensations to those experienced in the two previous experiments. Discuss the writings as a group. Add to your list any observations or comparisons mentioned by others that apply to you.

Analysis

1. What are some of the reasons for your great difficulty in standing on one foot with your eyes closed after spinning around five times?

2. Which plays a more important role in maintaining your balance, the sense of vision or the sense of equilibrium? Justify your choice.

Human Behavior Lab #2

What Happens to Our Ability to Taste Sweetness As We Age?

Introduction

You may have noticed that your grandparents, and possibly your parents, have been using more sugar than usual. Perhaps they are complaining that foods don't seem to taste as sweet as they used to years ago. They may think that food manufacturers are using less sugar to save money; however, some scientists claim that things happen to our sense of taste as we age. We may lose the sense of taste for sweetness, sourness, saltiness, or bitterness. We may have a diminished sense of taste, or possibly a distorted sense of taste (for example, a sweetener may taste salty).

You and a few other students your age will be the control group in an investigation that compares the ability of different age groups to detect sweeteners in a water solution. People between the ages of 35 and 50 are one experimental group, and persons between 51 and 69 are the second experimental group. The last experimental group will be made up of people 70 years old and older.

Materials

- 1g packets of artificial sweetener, such as Sweet'n Low® (10)
- 1-liter container
- Plastic test tubes (6)
- Paper for recording data
- Jars with lids for storing stock solutions (6)
- Labels (6)
- Test-tube racks
- Pen
- 100mL graduated cylinder
- Demineralized (spring) water
- Cotton swabs
- Stoppers for test tubes (6)
- Disposable paper cups

(continued)

Name _____ Date _____

What Happens to Our Ability to Taste
Sweetness As We Age? (continued)

Procedure

1. Your first step is to prepare a series of solutions that contain known amounts of sweetener. The first solution should be made as follows:

    a. Dissolve 1 gram of sweetener in 10mL of water.

    b. Pour into a stock solution jar and cover.

    c. Prepare a label that reads "10% Sweetener Solution." Paste the label on the jar.

2. Next prepare a 5% solution of sweetener as follows:

    a. Dissolve 1 gram of sweetener in 20mL of water.

    b. Pour into a stock solution jar and cover.

    c. Prepare a label that reads "5% Sweetener Solution." Paste the label on the jar.

3. Now prepare a 1.0% solution of sweetener:

    a. Dissolve 1 gram of sweetener in 100mL of water.

    b. Pour into a stock solution jar and cover.

    c. Prepare a label that reads "1.0% Sweetener Solution." Paste the label on the jar.

4. Next prepare a 0.5% solution of sweetener:

    a. Dissolve 1 gram of sweetener in 200mL of water.

    b. Pour into a stock solution jar and cover.

    c. Prepare a label that reads "0.5% Sweetener Solution." Paste the label on the jar.

5. Finally prepare a 0.1% solution of sweetener:

    a. Dissolve 1 gram of sweetener in 1,000mL of water.

    b. Pour into a stock solution jar and cover.

    c. Prepare a label that reads "0.1% Sweetener Solution." Paste the label on the jar.

(continued)

Human Behavior Lab #2

What Happens to Our Ability to Taste Sweetness As We Age? (continued)

6. Your last jar will be the control. It should contain only pure demineralized water or spring water.

7. When testing individuals, be sure to do the following:

   a. Transfer some of each stock solution to labeled, stoppered test tubes. Label the tubes #1, #2, and so on, rather than indicating their relative sweetness on the label. Make a record of the solution strengths by numbered tube. Carry the tubes as well as clean swabs with you.

   b. Ask friends, relatives, neighbors, or faculty members if they are willing to be subjects in a taste test. Explain that you are using a harmless, nonfattening food additive. **Don't tell the subjects that they should experience a sweet taste.**

   c. Try to get at least three subjects in each group. This might be difficult for the group of subjects over 70. Do your best!

   d. Give each subject a cup of water for rinsing out the mouth before each test (including the first test). Any leftover sweetness from a previous test or sweetness from leftover food should be removed.

   e. Apply the solutions in a random order; that is, don't start with the strongest solution first, then the next strongest, and so on.

   f. The swabs soaked in sweetener are to be applied to the taste buds for sensing sweetness. Look at the following diagram. Notice that the taste buds for sweetness are located in the front part of the tongue.

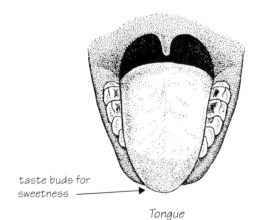

taste buds for sweetness ⟶

Tongue

(continued)

What Happens to Our Ability to Taste Sweetness As We Age? (continued)

g. Dip a swab into one of the test tubes, then place the moistened swab on the volunteer's tongue in the sweet-sensitive region and ask the person to describe the taste. **Use a swab only once, then discard it.** Ask each volunteer to gently rinse out his or her mouth between each swab test. Repeat the test with the remaining solutions.

h. Keep accurate records, marking a + when a sweet taste is reported and a – when not reported. A sample data recording sheet follows.

SAMPLE DATA RECORDING SHEET							
	Solutions + = sweet reported; – = sweet unreported						**Subject's Observations** **(distorted taste; little taste)**
	#1	**#2**	**#3**	**#4**	**#5**	**#6**	
Teenagers							
1.							
2.							
3.							
Ages 35–50							
1.							
2.							
3.							

(continued)

Human Behavior Lab #2

What Happens to Our Ability to Taste
Sweetness As We Age? (continued)

SAMPLE DATA RECORDING SHEET (*continued*)							
	Solutions + = sweet reported; – = sweet unreported						**Subject's Observations** (distorted taste; little taste)
	#1	**#2**	**#3**	**#4**	**#5**	**#6**	
Ages 51–69							
1.							
2.							
3.							
Ages 70 and older							
1.							
2.							
3.							

Analysis

1. Why should all subjects also be given plain water to taste?

2. What would be wrong with telling everyone they were going to taste a sweetener?

3. Why shouldn't the solutions be administered in order, from strongest to weakest or vice versa?

4. Why would it be better to have ten subjects in each group rather than three?

5. What conclusions can you draw from your data?

6. What are some ways in which the design of this investigation could be improved?

 25 Low-Cost Biology Investigations

Name _____ Date _____

What Happens to Our Ability to Taste Saltiness As We Age?

Introduction

This investigation will center around the aging process and the ability to taste salt. You will be encouraged to use more than one salt because specific sodium salts may taste saltier than other sodium salts. Older people may lose their salt taste completely, or they may just have a diminished sense of taste. It is also possible that their sense of taste is distorted and that salty foods may taste bitter or sour to them.

You and students of your age will be the control group in this investigation of people's ability to taste salty solutions. The other groups will be made up of people in different age groups. One experimental group will be composed of people between the ages of 35 and 50; another will be persons between 51 and 69; the last experimental group will be composed of people 70 years old and older.

Materials

- Sodium chloride
- Sodium sulfate*
- Sodium acetate*
- Sodium carbonate*
- 1-liter container
- Test tubes (6)

*Optional

- Paper for recording data
- Jars with lids for storing stock solutions (6)
- Labels (6)
- Test-tube racks
- Pen

- 100mL graduated cylinder
- Demineralized (spring) water
- Cotton swabs
- Stoppers for test tubes (6)
- Disposable paper cups

Procedure

1. Your first step is to prepare a series of sodium salt solutions. Make the first solution as follows:

   a. Dissolve 1 gram of salt in 10mL of water.

(continued)

Human Behavior Lab #3

What Happens to Our Ability to Taste
Saltiness As We Age? *(continued)*

b. Pour into a stock solution jar and cover.

c. Prepare a label that reads "10% Sodium _____ Solution" (fill in the blank with the type of salt used). Paste the label on the jar.

2. Next prepare a 5% solution of salt as follows:

a. Dissolve 1 gram of the salt in 20mL of water.

b. Pour into a stock solution jar and cover.

c. Prepare a label that reads "5% Sodium _____ Solution." Paste the label on the jar.

3. Now prepare a 1.0% solution:

a. Dissolve 1 gram of the salt in 100mL of water.

b. Pour into a stock solution jar and cover.

c. Prepare a label that reads "1.0% Sodium _____ Solution." Paste the label on the jar.

4. Next prepare a 0.5% solution:

a. Dissolve 1 gram of the salt in 200mL of water.

b. Pour into a stock solution jar and cover.

c. Prepare a label that reads "0.5% Sodium _____ Solution." Paste the label on the jar.

5. Finally prepare a 0.1% solution of salt:

a. Dissolve 1 gram of the salt in 1,000mL of water.

b. Pour into a stock solution jar and cover.

c. Prepare a label that reads "0.1% Sodium _____ Solution." Paste the label on the jar.

6. Your last jar is your control. It should contain only pure demineralized water or spring water.

(continued)

Name _____ Date _____

What Happens to Our Ability to Taste
Saltiness As We Age? *(continued)*

7. When testing individuals, be sure to do the following:

   a. Transfer some of each stock solution to labeled, stoppered test tubes. Label the tubes #1, #2, and so on. Do not indicate the relative salt strengths on the label. Make a record of the solution strengths by numbered tube. Carry the tubes as well as clean swabs with you.

   b. Ask friends, relatives, neighbors, or faculty members if they are willing to be subjects in a taste test. Explain that you are using a harmless, nonfattening food additive. **Don't tell the subjects that the solution should taste salty.**

   c. Try to get at least three subjects in each group. The more subjects you get the better. Try hard.

   d. Give each subject a cup of water for rinsing out the mouth before each test (including the first test). Each person's mouth must be free of any leftover food taste before testing.

   e. Apply the salt solutions in a random order; that is, don't start with the strongest solution first, then the next strongest, and so on.

   f. The swabs soaked in salt solution will be applied to the taste buds for sensing salts. Look at the following diagram. Notice that the taste buds for saltiness are located in the extreme forward part of the tongue and back along the left and right sides in a thin line.

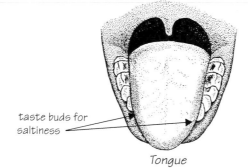

taste buds for saltiness

Tongue

   g. Dip a swab into one of the test tubes, then place the moistened swab on the subject's tongue. The best place to touch the tongue with the cotton swabs is in the middle of the very tip. Ask the subject if he or she detects a taste. If so, what taste is detected? **Use a swab only once and then discard it.** Ask each volunteer to rinse out his or her mouth between each swab test. Repeat the test with the remaining solutions.

(continued)

     25 Low-Cost Biology Investigations

Name _____ Date _____

What Happens to Our Ability to Taste
Saltiness As We Age? (*continued*)

h. Keep accurate records, marking a **+** when a salty taste is reported and a **–** when not reported. A sample data recording sheet follows.

SAMPLE DATA RECORDING SHEET							
	Solutions + = salt reported; – = salt unreported						**Subject's Observations** (distorted taste; little taste)
	#1	**#2**	**#3**	**#4**	**#5**	**#6**	
Teenagers							
1.							
2.							
3.							
Ages 35–50							
1.							
2.							
3.							
Ages 51–69							
1.							
2.							
3.							

(continued)

Name _____ Date _____

What Happens to Our Ability to Taste
Saltiness As We Age? (continued)

SAMPLE DATA RECORDING SHEET (*continued*)							
	Solutions + = salt reported; − = salt unreported						**Subject's Observations** (distorted taste; little taste)
	#1	**#2**	**#3**	**#4**	**#5**	**#6**	
Ages 70 and older							
1.							
2.							
3.							

Analysis

1. What conclusions can you draw from your data?

2. Repeat this investigation using one or more of the optional salts listed in the Materials section.

   a. Are the results the same for all the salts you used?

   b. Which salts were older people unable to detect?

   c. Which salts were detected by the oldest people?

Name _____ Date _____

What Happens to Our Ability to Taste Sourness As We Age?

Introduction

This investigation will center around the aging process and the ability to taste a sour substance. Various concentrations of lemon juice will be used.

You and students of your age will be the control group in this investigation of people's ability to taste sour solutions. The other groups will be made up of people in different age groups. One experimental group will be composed of people between the ages of 35 and 50; another will be persons between 51 and 69; the last experimental group will be composed of people 70 years old and older.

Materials

- 5mL graduated cylinder (optional: 1mL pipet)
- Medicine droppers (4)
- 100mL graduated cylinder
- Paper for recording data
- Jars with lids for storing stock solutions (5)
- Pen
- Juice squeezer
- Disposable paper cups
- Test-tube racks
- Lemon
- Demineralized (spring) water
- Test tubes (5)
- Cotton swabs
- Stoppers for test tubes (5)
- Labels (5)

Procedure

1. Your first step is to prepare a series of lemon juice solutions. Make the first solution as follows:

   a. Cut a lemon in half and squeeze the juice into a paper cup.

   b. Using a medicine dropper, collect and transfer 1mL of the juice into the 5mL graduated cylinder (if a pipet is used, transfer 1mL directly to the 100mL graduated cylinder). Collect only the juice; avoid including any lemon pulp.

(continued)

Human Behavior Lab #4

What Happens to Our Ability to Taste
Sourness As We Age? *(continued)*

    c. Pour the 1mL of juice into the 100mL graduated cylinder (if it isn't already in there).

    d. Add 99mL demineralized water. Pour the contents into a clean stock solution jar. Label the jar "Lemon Juice 1:100 Dilution."

2. Clean both graduated cylinders with water and then dry them thoroughly.

    a. Using a clean medicine dropper, collect 1mL of the 1:100 dilution solution and place it in the 5mL cylinder (if a pipet is used, transfer 1mL directly to the 100mL cylinder).

    b. Transfer the entire 1mL to the 100mL cylinder. Add 99mL of demineralized water. Go back to the 1:100 solution and stopper it before you forget.

    c. Pour the 100mL of solution you just prepared into a clean stock solution jar and label this solution "1:1,000 Dilution Solution."

3. Using the same technique, prepare a 1:10,000 dilution solution and then a 1:100,000 dilution.

4. Your fifth and last jar is your control. It should contain 100mL of pure demineralized water or spring water.

5. When testing individuals, be sure to do the following:

    a. Transfer some of each stock solution to labeled, stoppered test tubes. Label the tubes #1, #2, and so on. Do not indicate the relative strengths on the label. Make a record of the solution strengths by numbered tube. Carry the tubes as well as clean swabs with you.

    b. Ask friends, relatives, neighbors, or faculty members if they are willing to be subjects in a taste test. Explain that you are using a harmless, nonfattening food additive. **Don't tell the volunteers that the solution should have a sour taste.**

    c. Try to get at least three volunteers in each group. The more subjects you get the better. Try hard.

(continued)

Human Behavior Lab #4

What Happens to Our Ability to Taste
Sourness As We Age? (continued)

d. Give each subject a cup of water for rinsing out the mouth before each test (including the first test). Each person's mouth must be free of any leftover food taste before testing.

e. Apply the lemon juice solutions in a random order; that is, don't start with the strongest solution first, then the next strongest, and so on.

f. The swabs soaked in lemon juice will be applied to the taste buds for sensing sour substances. Look at the following diagram. Notice that these taste buds are located on the extreme edges of the tongue and extend back from the middle of the tongue to the very rear of the tongue in a thin line.

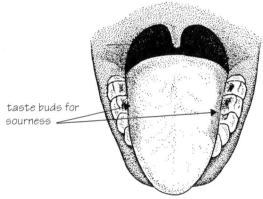

taste buds for sourness

Tongue

g. Dip a swab into one of the test tubes, then place the moistened swab on the subject's tongue. The best place to touch the tongue with the cotton swabs is behind the middle of the tongue and very close to the left or right edge. Ask the subject if he or she detects a taste. If so, what taste is detected? **Use a swab only once and then discard it.** Ask each volunteer to rinse out his or her mouth between each swab test. Repeat the test with the remaining solutions.

h. Keep accurate records, marking a + when a sour taste is reported and a − when not reported. A sample data recording sheet follows.

(continued)

       25 Low-Cost Biology Investigations

Name _____ Date _____

What Happens to Our Ability to Taste
Sourness As We Age? (continued)

	Solutions + = sour reported; − = sour unreported						Subject's observations (distorted taste; little taste)
SAMPLE DATA RECORDING SHEET							
	#1	#2	#3	#4	#5	#6	
Teenagers							
1.							
2.							
3.							
Ages 35–50							
1.							
2.							
3.							
Ages 51–69							
1.							
2.							
3.							

(continued)

Human Behavior Lab #4

What Happens to Our Ability to Taste
Sourness As We Age? (continued)

SAMPLE DATA RECORDING SHEET (continued)							
	Solutions + = sour reported; − = sour unreported						**Subject's Observations** **(distorted taste; little taste)**
	#1	**#2**	**#3**	**#4**	**#5**	**#6**	
Ages 70 and older							
1.							
2.							
3.							

Analysis

1. What conclusions can you draw from your data?

2. Repeat the investigation using other sour substances.

3. What can you conclude from this investigation?

4. If older people do lose their ability to taste sweets, salts, etc., what are the implications of this for food manufacturers?

5. Explain how our taste buds help us survive.

Name _____ Date _____

Human Behavior Lab #5

How Is Your Muscle Strength Affected by Exercise?

Introduction

In this investigation you will use yourself as an experimental subject. You are aware from everyday experience that when you perform a physical activity, you can do much more of it at the start. As time goes on, you slow down more and more. Coaches, keenly aware of this phenomenon, call for time-outs and often replace fatigued players with fresh ones.

This investigation will bring a new dimension to that familiar observation of feeling fatigue while exercising. You will make a scientific study of the fatigue factor in your upper-arm muscles. It is best to do this study with a partner who will act as timekeeper and counter as well as recorder. After you have completed your investigation, exchange roles with your partner.

Materials

- Chair
- Watch (or clock) with second hand
- Data table (see sample)
- Heavy book (dictionary, textbook)
- Long table (kitchen, dining room)
- Pen or pencil

Procedure

1. Sit in a chair in front of the table. Place your timepiece nearby so that the seconds can be counted easily. Place the book on the table in front of you.

2. Bend the upper part of your body and slump forward so that one entire arm (up to the shoulder) is resting on the table. Move your chair so that you are comfortable. Keep the palm side of your extended hand facing up. With your other hand, place the heavy book in your extended arm's hand and hold the book tightly with your thumb and fingers.

3. Begin to time 30 seconds and to lift the book toward you.

(continued)

Human Behavior Lab #5

How Is Your Muscle Strength Affected by Exercise? (continued)

4. Count the number of times you can lift your forearm to a vertical position while holding the book. Be sure your upper arm remains in contact with the table all the while.

5. You or your partner should then record the number of arm lifts completed in the data table. Use the space for session #1.

6. After you or your partner records the data, *immediately* repeat the arm lift exercise for another 30 seconds. Record this data in the space for session #2. Don't rest in between sessions (except for the time it takes to enter your data if you are doing this investigation without a partner).

7. Repeat the lifting of the book for eight additional 30-second sessions. Be sure to record the data after each session. No resting!

DATA TABLE			
Session	**Number of Arm Lifts in 30 Seconds**	**Session**	**Number of Arm Lifts in 30 Seconds**
#1		#6	
#2		#7	
#3		#8	
#4		#9	
#5		#10	

(continued)

Human Behavior Lab #5

How Is Your Muscle Strength Affected
by Exercise? (continued)

Analysis

1. Chart your results on the graph provided. Plot the number of sessions on the horizontal axis. Use an appropriate scale to represent the number of arm lifts on the vertical axis.

Effect of fatigue upon arm muscle action

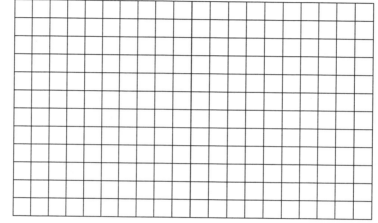

number of arm lifts
in 30 seconds

session

2. Does your graph reveal a steady loss of muscle power due to fatigue?

3. After which session was the loss of muscle power the greatest?

4. What conclusions can you draw concerning the effect of fatigue upon muscle power?

5. Repeat this investigation using the other hand. Are the results the same? Explain.

Name _____ Date _____

How Is Your Muscle Strength Affected by Temperature?

Introduction

In this investigation you will use yourself as an experimental subject. Even though we are warm-blooded, we are affected by extremes in temperature. You feel uncomfortable in cold, chilly weather as well as in hot, humid weather. In both cases, you may experience problems when exercising vigorously. Because it is easier to control cold, that will be the temperature extreme used for this investigation.

Materials

- Water
- Timer (watch or clock with second hand)
- Ice cubes
- Towel
- Pail (or bucket)
- Rubber band
- Moistened kitchen sponge or tennis ball
- Thermometer

Procedure

1. Determine the room air temperature using the thermometer. Record this information in the data table on the following page.

2. Fold the moist sponge in half and use the rubber band to keep it in the folded position. Place the folded sponge (or tennis ball) so that it fits comfortably in one hand. Now tightly close your fist.

3. While watching the second hand of your timer, count the number of times you can open and close your fist in 30 seconds. To do this investigation properly, open your hand fully so that your fingers are stretched out as far as possible, then make a fist as fast as you can. Try to move your hand as rapidly as possible. Make as many fists as you can in 30 seconds.

4. Record the number of times you opened and closed your fist during the 30-second interval.

(continued)

Human Behavior Lab #6

How Is Your Muscle Strength Affected
by Temperature? (*continued*)

5. Half fill the pail with water and ice. Be sure you use sufficient ice, enough to last for five minutes without melting completely. Wait two or three minutes, allowing the water temperature to reach 10°–15°C. Record the temperature in the data table.

6. Next grip the folded sponge or tennis ball in the same hand as before. Immerse your closed fist, up to the wrist, in the ice water. Keep your fist closed for 10 seconds. Now, begin to open and close your fist as rapidly as you can for the next 30 seconds. Record your data in the table.

7. Remove and dry your hand with the towel. Add more ice to the pail. When your hand is no longer cold, repeat step 6, but this time keep your fist closed for 20 seconds before you begin to open and close your hand. Enter your results in the data table. **If at any time your hand becomes so cold that it hurts, remove it from the water at once and stop the investigation.**

8. Repeat the procedure of drying your hand, allowing it to return to its normal temperature, and then executing step 6. This time keep your fist immersed for 30 seconds in the ice water before you start to open and close your fist. **If at any time your hand becomes so cold that it hurts, remove it from the water at once and stop the investigation.**

DATA TABLE		
Temperature		**Number of Fists Made in 30 Seconds**
Air: °C		
Ice water: °C (10-second trial)		
Ice water: °C (20-second trial)		
Ice water: °C (30-second trial)		

Analysis

1. What was the effect of ice-cold water on your ability to open and close your fist repeatedly?

2. Repeat this investigation using your other hand. Are your results the same, similar, or different?

Name _____   Date _____

How Much Perspiration Is Excreted from One Hand?

Introduction

Our bodies excrete perspiration in amounts that may surprise you. In this investigation you will discover how much perspiration your hand produces in a short time. Perspiration consists of water, a small amount of salt, and a tiny amount of urea (a nitrogenous waste material).

Materials

- Plastic storage bags (2) (1-gallon size, not the sealing or locking type)
- Graduated pipet (5mL) or graduated cylinder (10mL)
- Masking tape
- Centimeter rule

Procedure

1. Place one hand into one of the plastic bags.

2. Seal the bag with masking tape by wrapping the tape around the bag at your wrist. The bag should be airtight but comfortable. Comfort is more important than the bag being airtight.

3. Keep the plastic bag on your wrist for 15 minutes. You can sit quietly and read while you wait.

4. After 15 minutes, remove the plastic bag. Be careful not to spill the perspiration that has accumulated in the bag.

5. Using either the pipet or the graduated cylinder, measure the amount of perspiration your hand produced. In 15 minutes the amount of perspiration produced was _____ mL. Thus _____ mL would be produced in one hour.

(continued)

Human Perspiration Lab

How Much Perspiration Is Excreted from One Hand? (continued)

6. Calculate the approximate number of square centimeters of skin on the hand you used. To do this:

   a. Bring your thumb and fingers together.

   b. Measure the length and width of your hand, then multiply the two measurements together.

   c. Double the number to account for the fact that there are two sides to your hand.

   To make this task easier, ignore the thickness of your hand. Fill in the following blanks. My hand measures _____ cm^2 of skin. The amount of perspiration excreted from 1 square centimeter of skin in one hour is _____ mL.

7. Repeat the experiment using the other plastic bag. This time, however, exercise for five minutes before enclosing your hand in the plastic bag. One exercise you can do, even in a classroom, is deep knee bends. Just stand in the aisle next to your desk and squat down with your hands on your thighs. Go up and down, bending your knees as fast as you can, for five minutes. Compare these perspiration results to those you obtained when you were at rest.

   The amount of perspiration collected in the bag after five minutes of exercising was _____ mL. The amount that would be excreted in one hour would be _____ mL. My hand contains _____ cm^2 of skin. The amount of perspiration excreted from 1 square centimeter in one hour, after exercising, would be _____ mL.

Oil Spill Lab #1

Cleaning Up an Aquatic Oil Spill

Introduction

In January 1991 the largest oil spill in history occurred when oil was released from Kuwaiti storage tanks in Iraq into the Persian Gulf. Some estimates of the spill run as high as 450 million gallons of crude oil. The oil moved southward from Iraq along the coast of Saudi Arabia. In some places the oil was so thick that it looked like mud. Some of the oil floating on top of the water formed tar balls, which in time will sink to the bottom of the Persian Gulf. Eventually, the currents will wash these balls of tar onto the beaches of Saudi Arabia.

This investigation will point out the problems and the difficulties of trying to clean up an aquatic oil spill on a very small scale. You will determine the effectiveness of various materials that could be used to remove oil from the surface of the water. You will also investigate the effect of stormy seas on the cleanup of an oil spill.

Materials

- Vegetable (cooking) oil (approximately 25mL)
- Shallow aluminum pan (such as from a TV dinner)
- String
- Paper cups
- Paper towels
- Detergent (liquid)
- Any absorbent material (old loose-leaf paper, newspaper, a returned test, etc.)
- Scissors
- Ruler
- Cloth rag
- Toothpicks (2)
- Bath soap
- Water
- Drinking straws (2)
- Dry breakfast cereal (such as Corn Flakes®)
- Graduated cylinder (10mL)
- Tablespoon
- Cotton balls
- Sponge
- Sawdust

Procedure

1. Pour approximately 5mL of oil into the graduated cylinder.

(continued)

Oil Spill Lab #1

Cleaning Up an Aquatic Oil Spill (*continued*)

2. Fill the shallow aluminum pan about 1cm deep with water.

3. Tie the ends of a piece of string together so that you form a loop with an approximate diameter of 10cm. This will be your *boom* (a floating barrier used to contain floating oil and prevent it from spreading over a large area).

4. Float the boom (loop of string) in the center of the pan.

5. Pour a small quantity of oil on the water in the center of the boom. What kind of oil did you use? _____

   Did all of the oil float on the surface or did some of it sink below the surface of the water?

   How effective was the string in preventing the oil from spreading over the entire

   surface of the water? _____

6. Use the tablespoon as a *skimmer* and try to skim the oil off the surface of the water

   inside the boom. How effective is skimming? _____

7. Use a toothpick to remove the boom (string loop). Discard both the toothpick and the string.

8. Add a little more oil to the water in the center of the pan. Pour the oil slowly and add just enough to cover the surface of the entire pan.

9. Attempt to clean up the oil spill using each of the materials in the chart on page 45. Use one item at a time. When necessary, add more oil. Complete the chart by indicating how well or how poorly each material cleaned up the spill. Use terms such as "Not effective at all," "Slightly effective," "Poor," "Fair," "Good," "Very good," "Excellent."

(continued)

Oil Spill Lab #1

Cleaning Up an Aquatic Oil Spill (*continued*)

EFFECTIVENESS OF MATERIAL	
Material	**Evaluation**
Paper toweling	
Cotton balls	
Cloth rag	
Sponge	
Detergent and paper towels	
Sponge and detergent	
Rag and bath soap	
Sawdust	
Dry cereal	
Other material:	

According to your results, which is the better method for cleaning up an oil spill, absorbing or skimming? _____

10. Again cover the surface of the water with oil. Now gently blow through the two drinking straws. Direct the air stream across the surface of the oil spill. Using your most effective material, try to clean up the oil spill. On the basis of this experiment, is it easier or harder to clean up an oil spill on a windy day? _____ What evidence do you have for your conclusion?_____

_____

_____

_____

This ends the investigation. To clean up, place the solid wastes in the garbage pail, add a few drops of detergent to the vegetable oil–water mixture and shake well, then discard in the sink.

Oil Spill Lab #2

What Are the Effects of an Aquatic Oil Spill on Sea Birds' Feathers?

Introduction

In the spring of 1989 an oil tanker named the *Exxon Valdez* hit some rocks in Prince William Sound off the coast of Alaska. More than ten million gallons of crude oil spilled into the sound. As a result of this accident, the oil soon washed up on the beaches along the coastline. Some of the beaches that were polluted were hundreds of miles away from the rocks that ripped into the hull of the *Valdez*. Despite the efforts of many people using modern equipment, only 10% of the oil was removed through cleanup efforts.

The deadly effects of the crude oil on plants and animals are still in evidence. The oil caused the deaths of seals, otters, and birds as well as microscopic plants and animals. Fish, such as herring and salmon, were barely affected because they could swim away from the oil-contaminated water.

The oil affected sea birds in a number of ways, and unless these birds were quickly found and cleansed of oil by rescue workers, they died. In this investigation you will discover why an aquatic oil spill is so harmful to sea birds.

***Caution:* Do not participate in this investigation if you are allergic to feathers.**

Materials

- Feathers (from a feather pillow)
- Paper cups (2)
- Water
- Liquid detergent (for cleanup)
- Paper towels
- Vegetable oil

Procedure

1. Half fill one of the paper cups with clean water. Half fill a second cup with oil. Immerse one feather in the cup of water. Examine it carefully. Write your observations of this feather: _____

   _____

   _____

(continued)

Oil Spill Lab #2

What Are the Effects of an Aquatic Oil Spill on Sea Birds' Feathers? (continued)

If a bird's feathers do become wet with water, what does the bird instinctively do to dry its feathers? (*Hint:* How do birds in a birdbath dry themselves?)_____

_____

What physical process is responsible for the drying? _____

_____

_____

2. Predict what you will observe if you dip a feather into oil: _____

_____

_____

Was your prediction correct? _____

3. Why can't birds rid their feathers of oil in the same way that they rid them of water?

_____

4. What effect do you think a coating of oil would have on an aquatic bird's ability to fly?

_____

Justify your answer: _____

5. What effect do you think an oil spill would have on an aquatic bird's ability to feed on underwater plants and animals? _____

_____

Justify your answer: _____

6. What effect do you think a coating of oil would have on an aquatic bird's ability to swim?

Justify your answer: _____

Oil Spill Lab #3

What Are the Effects of Oil-Soaked Feathers on the Body Temperature of Sea Birds?

Introduction

This investigation will illustrate an oil spill's deadly effect on sea birds. You will investigate the effect of oil-soaked feathers upon the body temperature of sea birds.

This lab requires a large amount of feathers, which can be obtained from an old feather pillow or quilt.

Caution: **Don't participate in this investigation if you are allergic to feathers.**

Materials

- Feathers (from a feather pillow)
- Scissors
- Small sandwich-size plastic bags (2)
- Paper cups (2)
- Balance
- Thermometers (2)
- Water
- Liquid detergent (for cleanup)
- 500mL beakers
- Rubber bands (2)
- Paper towels
- Vegetable oil
- Ice cubes

Procedure

1. Check your thermometers to be sure that both show the same room air temperature. If not, record the amount by which they differ. Then, when taking readings, be sure to adjust for the difference. For example, if one thermometer reads 20°C and the other reads 22°C, subtract 2° from all readings of the thermometer that gave the higher reading.

2. Place a small plastic bag on the balance and weight it. Add 2.5g to what the bag weighs by adjusting the rider if it is a triple-beam balance.

(continued)

 25 Low-Cost Biology Investigations

Oil Spill Lab #3

What Are the Effects of Oil-Soaked Feathers
on the Body Temperature of Sea Birds?
(continued)

3. Fill the plastic bag with 2.5g of feathers and push the feathers down into the bottom of the bag.

4. Place one of the thermometers into the bag so that the bulb rests in the middle of the feathers. Seal the bag with a rubber band that will also hold the thermometer in place.

5. Weigh the second plastic bag and fill it with 2.5g of feathers. Push these feathers toward the bottom of the bag.

6. Half fill one of the beakers with oil. Add just enough oil to soak the feathers in this second bag.

7. While holding the opening of this bag almost closed, pour off the excess oil into a suitable container. Don't let the feathers escape from the bag. Gently squeeze the oil-soaked feathers inside the plastic bag and pour off as much of the excess oil as you can.

8. Place the second thermometer inside this bag so that its bulb rests in the middle of the oil-soaked feathers. Seal this bag with a rubber band that will hold the thermometer in place.

9. Half fill both beakers with ice cubes and cold water. Wait about three minutes until the temperatures in both beakers become equalized.

10. Place one bag of feathers in each beaker.

11. Read the thermometers every two minutes for a ten-minute period. Complete the data table on the following page.

(continued)

Oil Spill Lab #3

What Are the Effects of Oil-Soaked Feathers
on the Body Temperature of Sea Birds?
(continued)

DATA TABLE		
Time	**Temperature of Dry Feathers (in °C)**	**Temperature of Oil-Soaked Feathers (in °C)**
0 min		
2 min		
4 min		
6 min		
8 min		
10 min		

12. What conclusions can you draw from your data? _____

_____

_____

_____

_____

13. Why might sea birds whose feathers are soaked with oil freeze in cold weather?

_____

_____

_____

     25 Low-Cost Biology Investigations

Name _____ Date _____

How Much Oxygen Do Germinating Seeds Consume in 15 Minutes?

Introduction

All aerobic organisms take in oxygen and give off carbon dioxide as long as they are alive. This is true for plants as well as animals. Some organisms have elaborate structures such as lungs or tracheal tubes for exchanging respiratory gases; others merely use moist membranes. If you place a living organism in a closed system, it is possible to measure its consumption of oxygen. To do this, you will need a *respirometer*, which you can easily construct.

Your first task will be to understand the operation of the respirometer. The second task will be to construct it.

Materials

- Large test tube
- Metric ruler
- Petroleum jelly (optional)
- Germinating dandelion seeds (or any germinating seeds) (1g)
- One-hole stopper
- Rigid polyethylene tubing or hollow glass tubing (20cm long) bent at a right angle
- Limewater
- Medicine dropper
- Support stand and clamp or several thick books
- Wad of cotton
- Glycerine
- Marking crayon
- Weighing paper
- Liquid detergent
- Balance
- Paper towels
- Spatula
- Transparent tape

(continued)

Respiration Lab #1

How Much Oxygen Do Germinating Seeds Consume in 15 Minutes? (continued)

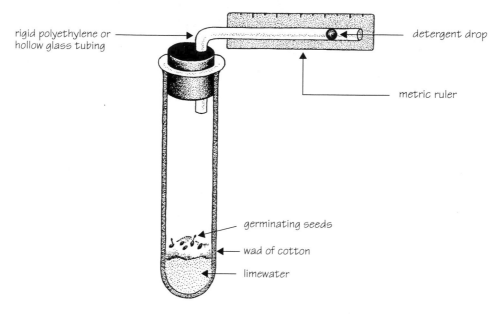

rigid polyethylene or hollow glass tubing

detergent drop

metric ruler

germinating seeds

wad of cotton

limewater

Respirometer containing germinating seeds

Procedure

1. Examine the diagram of the respirometer. If you don't have a piece of tubing bent at a right angle as shown, you can use two pieces of straight tubing (one long and one short) connected by a piece of rubber tubing to form the right angle. There must be no air leaks in the respirometer. If you use the two pieces connected with a piece of rubber tubing, apply a small amount of petroleum jelly at the connecting points to ensure an airtight seal.

2. Pour a small amount of glycerine into the stopper hole. (The glycerine acts as a lubricant, making it easier to insert the tubing.) Insert the polyethylene or glass tubing into the one-hole stopper. If you are using glass, it is important to wrap a paper towel around the tubing to prevent injury if the glass breaks as you insert it.

(continued)

Respiration Lab #1

How Much Oxygen Do Germinating Seeds
Consume in 15 Minutes? *(continued)*

3. With your marking crayon, draw a line 0.5cm above the bottom of the test tube. Add limewater to the tube until it is filled to the crayon mark. As any living organism in the tube uses oxygen, carbon dioxide will be excreted. The carbon dioxide will then be absorbed by the limewater, creating a slight vacuum in the respirometer. This partial vacuum will draw a drop of liquid detergent in the glass tubing *inward*. This movement will be measured in millimeters using a metric ruler taped to the glass tubing.

4. Moisten a small wad of loose cotton and place it on top of the limewater. Then place the gram of germinating seeds on top of the moistened cotton. (The cotton is moistened because the germinating seeds require constant moisture.)

5. Tape the metric ruler to the tubing so that it looks like the diagram. With a medicine dropper, add a drop of detergent to the tubing. This drop should be near the end of the tubing (as shown).

6. Insert the stopper and tubing into the test tube. Do this *carefully*. Avoid spilling the detergent drop inside the tube as you carry out this step. Press down firmly on the stopper to make an airtight seal. If necessary, use a smear of petroleum jelly as a sealant on the rim of the test tube before inserting the stopper. Keep the setup in an upright position. A support stand and clamps are best for this purpose since they will keep the setup from moving about and the detergent drop from changing position. If no support stand and clamps are available, you can stack several books as a support system. Avoid moving the setup once it is in place.

7. Wait five minutes before taking your initial reading. There will be some CO_2 inside the respirometer when it is assembled. This must be absorbed before any measurements involving the germinating seeds can be taken. Take the initial reading wherever the drop of detergent is with respect to the metric ruler. Always take your measurements using the same part of the detergent drop—for example, the left edge of the drop. Record your initial reading in the data table on the following page.

8. Take readings every minute for 15 minutes and record them in the data table.

(continued)

Name _____ Date _____

Respiration Lab #1

How Much Oxygen Do Germinating Seeds
Consume in 15 Minutes? *(continued)*

DATA TABLE			
Initial reading: _____ (mm)			
Minute	**Movement (mm)**	**Minute**	**Movement (mm)**
1		9	
2		10	
3		11	
4		12	
5		13	
6		14	
7		15	
8			

Analysis

1. How does the respiration rate of a gram of germinating dandelion seeds compare with the respiration rate of a gram of fast-germinating plant seeds such as *Brassica rapa* seeds?

2. Compare the respiration rate of germinating dandelion seeds to an equal weight of germinating vegetable seeds (for example, squash seeds) that are much larger than dandelion seeds.

3. Is there a relationship between temperature and the respiration rate of germinating seeds? (Use germinating seeds of your choice.)

Name _____ Date _____

Land Crustacean Lab

Observing a Living Land Crustacean

Introduction

Most people think of lobsters, crabs, and shrimp as the only crustaceans. But there are amphibious and land crustaceans as well. The amphibious beach fleas, known as *scuds*, live on ocean beaches and feed on seaweed at low tide. There are approximately 100 species of land crustaceans living north of Mexico that feed on humus and fungi. Collectively they are called *wood lice*. *Pill bugs* and *sow bugs* are just two kinds of wood lice. Some species of wood lice are cosmopolitan; that is, they live in many parts of the world and in varied ecological conditions. Some are found only in wet places under rocks or pieces of wood, and others prefer to live in the damp basements of buildings.

Crustaceans have a hard yet flexible shell, or crust, and two pair of antennae. These organisms breathe by means of *gills*; some wood lice also have air-breathing organs called *tracheal* (breathing) *tubes* on the outside of their abdominal legs.

Wood lice feed on decaying vegetation and soft fleshy living plants. They replace the water evaporated from their bodies with water contained in their food. Only on damp nights will they leave their moist, protected homes. For this investigation you can use any land crustacean that lives in your area.

Materials

- Hand lens
- Glass jar containing moist soil and grass
- Moist paper towels
- Ice cube
- Land crustaceans (3 or more)
- Petri dish (top or bottom half)
- Forceps
- Probe

Procedure

1. Use forceps to remove the land crustaceans from their temporary home (the jar containing moist soil and grass). Do your best not to injure these tiny creatures. Place them in the center of the petri dish half.

(continued)

Land Crustacean Lab

Observing a Living Land Crustacean
(*continued*)

2. Use the hand lens to examine the animals carefully. Where are the antennae located? How many legs do they have? _____

3. In order to examine the animals easily, it is best to slow down the creatures' movements by inducing *hypothermia* (a lower-than-normal body temperature). To do this, begin by wrapping an ice cube in a moist paper towel.

4. Place the wrapped ice cube near the wood lice. Keep the ice as close to the animals as you can. In a short time, they will slow down.

5. Flip the animals over on their backs so that their *ventral* (belly) sides are facing you. Examine your wood lice until you find a female. Females have a pouch on the underside of their abdomens in which eggs and the newly hatched young are carried for a few days. The pouch is close to the *posterior* (rear) end of the animal. Describe the size and appearance of the pouch, which is called a *marsupium*:

   _____

   _____

   _____

6. The gills are on the legs and can be located if you look close to the point where the legs join the body. Think of the gills as being inside the armpits of the wood louse. Search for them using a hand lens or a stereomicroscope. Describe the gills to the best of your ability (try for accuracy and completeness): _____

   _____

   _____

   Look at the last pair of legs. (Remember that the legs form a water-conducting tube.) Describe their appearance: _____

   _____

(continued)

Land Crustacean Lab

Observing a Living Land Crustacean
(*continued*)

7. The wood louse is a terrestrial animal that must live in water. Explain this statement:

    _____

    _____

    _____

8. Using the eraser end of a pencil, gently poke an actively moving wood louse. **Be
    gentle. If you poke too hard, the wood louse will give off a foul-smelling
    substance.** What is its reaction to the stimulus? _____

    _____

    _____

9. Now can you determine why these creatures are called *pill bugs*? _____

    _____

    _____

10. One reason for rolling into a ball is protection from being eaten by ants or milli-
    pedes. What might be a second survival advantage of being able to roll into a ball?

    _____

    _____

    _____

11. Wood lice are *land isopods*. What does *isopod* mean? _____

    _____

    _____

Respiration Lab #2

How Much Oxygen Do Land Crustaceans Consume in 15 Minutes?

Introduction

In this investigation you will determine the amount of oxygen consumed by land crustaceans during 15 minutes.

All aerobic organisms take in oxygen and give off carbon dioxide as long as they are alive. This is true for plants as well as animals. Some organisms have elaborate structures such as lungs or tracheal tubes for exchanging respiratory gases; others merely use moist membranes. If you place a living organism in a closed system, it is possible to measure its consumption of oxygen. To do this, you will need a *respirometer*, which you can easily construct.

Your first task will be to understand the operation of the respirometer. The second task will be to construct it.

Materials

- Large test tube
- Metric ruler
- Petroleum jelly (optional)
- Land crustaceans (e.g., sow bugs) (1g)
- One-hole stopper
- Beaker (100mL)
- Forceps
- Rigid polyethylene tubing or hollow glass tubing (20cm long), bent at a right angle
- Limewater
- Medicine dropper
- Support stand and clamp or several thick books
- Wad of cotton
- Glycerine
- Marking crayon
- Liquid detergent
- Balance
- Paper towels
- Spatula
- Transparent tape

(continued)

Respiration Lab #2

How Much Oxygen Do Land Crustaceans Consume in 15 Minutes? (continued)

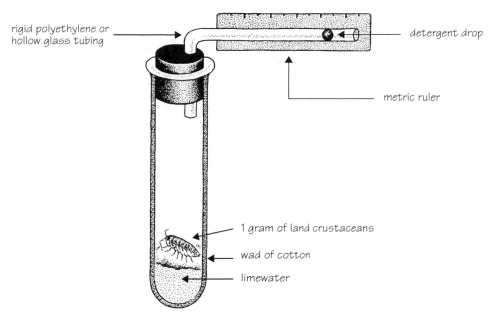

rigid polyethylene or hollow glass tubing

detergent drop

metric ruler

1 gram of land crustaceans

wad of cotton

limewater

Respirometer containing land crustaceans

Procedure

1. Make the respirometer as shown in the diagram above. If you don't have a piece of tubing bent at a right angle as shown, you can use two pieces of straight tubing (one long and one short) connected by a piece of rubber tubing to form the right angle. There must be no air leaks in the respirometer. If you use the two pieces connected with a piece of rubber tubing, apply a small amount of petroleum jelly at the connecting points to ensure an airtight seal.

2. Pour a small amount of glycerine into the stopper hole. (The glycerine acts as a lubricant, making it easier to insert the tubing.) Insert the polyethylene or glass tubing into the one-hole stopper. If you are using glass, it is important to wrap a paper towel around the tubing to prevent injury if the glass breaks as you insert it.

(continued)

   25 Low-Cost Biology Investigations

Respiration Lab #2

How Much Oxygen Do Land Crustaceans Consume in 15 Minutes? (*continued*)

3. With your marking crayon, draw a line 0.5cm above the bottom of the test tube. Add limewater to the tube until it is filled to the crayon mark. As any living organism in the tube uses oxygen, carbon dioxide will be excreted. The carbon dioxide will then be absorbed by the limewater, creating a slight vacuum in the respirometer. This partial vacuum will draw a drop of liquid detergent in the glass tubing *inward*. This movement will be measured in millimeters using a metric ruler taped to the glass tubing.

4. Moisten a wad of loose cotton and place it on top of the limewater. Land crustaceans need moisture as well as oxygen.

5. Weigh the beaker and then add 1g to its weight. Now add the land crustaceans, one by one, using forceps to transfer the animals. When you have 1 gram of living land crustaceans in the beaker, transfer them to the respirometer. Place them on top of the moist cotton wad.

6. Tape the metric ruler to the tubing so that it looks like the diagram. With a medicine dropper, add a drop of detergent to the tubing. This drop should be near the end of the tubing (as shown).

7. Insert the stopper and tubing into the test tube. Do this *carefully*. Avoid spilling the detergent drop inside the tube. Press down firmly on the stopper to make an airtight seal. If necessary, use a smear of petroleum jelly as a sealant on the rim of the test tube before inserting the stopper. Keep the setup in an upright position. If possible, use a support stand and clamps for this. They are best for this purpose. If no support stand and clamps are available, you can stack several books as a support system. Don't move the setup once it is in place.

8. Wait five minutes before taking your initial reading. During this time the CO_2 that was inside the respirometer when it was assembled will be absorbed.

9. Take the initial reading wherever the drop of detergent is with respect to the metric ruler after the five-minute waiting period. Always take your measurements using the same part of the detergent drop—for example, the left edge of the drop. Write down the initial reading in the table on the following page.

10. Take readings every minute for 15 minutes and record them in the data table.

(*continued*)

Respiration Lab #2

How Much Oxygen Do Land Crustaceans Consume in 15 Minutes? (continued)

DATA TABLE			
Initial reading: _____ (mm)			
Minute	**Movement (mm)**	**Minute**	**Movement (mm)**
1		9	
2		10	
3		11	
4		12	
5		13	
6		14	
7		15	
8			

Analysis

1. Is there a relationship between the temperature and the respiration rate of land crustaceans?

2. Carry out this investigation once in the morning and again in the afternoon. Is time of day a factor that affects the respiration rate of land crustaceans?

Name _____   Date _____

How Much Oxygen Do Adult House Crickets Consume in 15 Minutes?

Introduction

In this investigation you will determine how much oxygen is consumed by house crickets in 15 minutes. House crickets can be found in warm rooms such as kitchens and furnace rooms because they prefer a temperature of 31°C. Since house crickets are inexpensive, it would be wiser to purchase them from a biological supply company rather than try to collect them on your own. After this investigation is completed, the crickets should be added to the school's collection of living organisms. Crickets also make good pets (a common practice in Asia). Crickets are clean, odorless, and easy to feed and care for.

All aerobic organisms take in oxygen and give off carbon dioxide as long as they are alive. This is true for plants as well as animals. Some organisms have elaborate structures such as lungs or tracheal tubes for exchanging respiratory gases; others merely use moist membranes. If you place a living organism in a closed system, it is possible to measure its consumption of oxygen. To do this, you will need a *respirometer*, which you can easily construct.

Your first task will be to understand the operation of the respirometer. The second task will be to construct it.

Materials

- Large test tube
- Metric ruler
- Petroleum jelly (optional)
- Adult house crickets (1g)
- One-hole stopper
- Beaker (100mL)
- Forceps
- Rigid polyethylene tubing or hollow glass tubing (20cm long) bent at a right angle
- Limewater
- Medicine dropper
- Support stand and clamp or several thick books
- Wad of cotton
- Glycerine
- Marking crayon
- Liquid detergent
- Balance
- Paper towels
- Spatula
- Transparent tape
- Cage for crickets (available from biological supply companies)

(continued)

Name _____ Date _____

How Much Oxygen Do Adult House Crickets Consume in 15 Minutes? *(continued)*

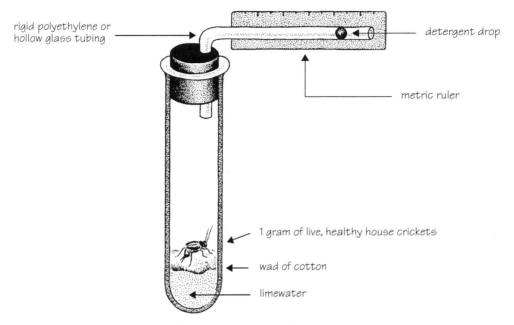

Respirometer containing house crickets

Procedure

1. Make the respirometer as shown in the diagram above. If you don't have a piece of tubing bent at a right angle as shown, you can use two pieces of straight tubing (one long and one short) connected by a piece of rubber tubing to form the right angle. There must be no air leaks in the respirometer. If you use the two pieces connected with a piece of rubber tubing, apply a small amount of petroleum jelly at the connecting points to ensure an airtight seal.

2. Pour a small amount of glycerine into the stopper hole. (The glycerine acts as a lubricant, making it easier to insert the tubing.) Insert the polyethylene or glass tubing into the one-hole stopper. If you are using glass, it is important to wrap a paper towel around the tubing to prevent injury if the glass breaks as you insert it.

(continued)

Respiration Lab #3

How Much Oxygen Do Adult House Crickets Consume in 15 Minutes? *(continued)*

3. With your marking crayon, draw a line 0.5cm above the bottom of the test tube. Add limewater to the tube until it is filled to the crayon mark. As any living organism in the tube uses oxygen, carbon dioxide will be excreted. The carbon dioxide will then be absorbed by the limewater, creating a slight vacuum in the respirometer. This partial vacuum will draw a drop of liquid detergent in the glass tubing *inward*. This movement will be measured in millimeters using a metric ruler taped to the glass tubing.

4. Place a wad of loose cotton on top of the limewater.

5. Weigh the beaker, then add 1g to its weight. Now add crickets, one by one, until you have 1 gram of live crickets. It is possible that one cricket will weigh more than 1 gram; it might weigh 1.25g. This is not a problem. Merely divide the amount of detergent-drop movement for each reading by 1.25. Place the crickets on top of the cotton wad.

6. Tape the metric ruler to the tubing so that it looks like the diagram. With a medicine dropper, add a drop of detergent to the tubing. This drop should be near the end of the tubing (as shown).

7. Insert the stopper into the test tube. Do this *carefully*. Avoid spilling the detergent drop inside the tube. Press down firmly on the stopper to make an airtight seal. If necessary, use a smear of petroleum jelly as a sealant on the rim of the test tube. Keep the setup in an upright position. It is best to use a support stand and clamps for this. If no support stand and clamps are available, stack several books as a support system. Don't move the setup once it is in place.

8. Wait five minutes before taking your initial reading. The CO_2 already inside the respirometer will be absorbed during this time.

9. Take the initial reading wherever the drop of detergent is with respect to the metric ruler after the five-minute waiting period. Always take your measurements using the same part of the detergent drop, for example, the left edge of the drop. Write down your initial reading in the table on the following page.

10. Take readings every minute for 15 minutes and record them in the data table on page 66.

(continued)

Respiration Lab #3

How Much Oxygen Do Adult House Crickets Consume in 15 Minutes? (continued)

11. Return the crickets to their cage or place of confinement. If you are not going to keep the crickets, observe and record information concerning their anatomy now. In particular, observe and record the following:

a. body—shape and size of head and abdomen _____
    _____
    _____
    _____
    _____

b. antennae—position and size _____
    _____
    _____

c. eyes—size and position _____
    _____
    _____

d. number of walking legs _____
    _____
    _____

e. mouth and surrounding parts—describe _____
    _____
    _____
    _____

f. breathing openings (*spiracles*) on the sides of the abdomen—number on each side
    _____
    _____

(continued)

Respiration Lab #3

How Much Oxygen Do Adult House Crickets Consume in 15 Minutes? (continued)

DATA TABLE			
Initial reading: _____ (mm)			
Minute	**Movement (mm)**	**Minute**	**Movement (mm)**
1		9	
2		10	
3		11	
4		12	
5		13	
6		14	
7		15	
8			

Analysis

1. Repeat this investigation using only crickets of one sex, then again using crickets of the other sex. Is there a significant difference in the oxygen consumption of males as compared to females? Explain your answer. Be sure to include supporting data.

2. Repeat the experiment at room temperature and at 15°C below room temperature. Is there a significant difference in the respiration rate?

Respiration Lab #4

How Much Oxygen Do House Cricket Nymphs Consume in 15 Minutes?

Introduction

In this investigation you will determine the amount of oxygen consumed by house cricket nymphs in 15 minutes. The young cricket, known as a *nymph*, hatches from the egg. The nymph resembles the adult. Nymphs grow rapidly as a result of the large quantities of food they consume. As they grow, they outgrow their outer skeletons and shed them, then they form new and larger outer coverings (*exoskeletons*). This process is called *molting*. Crickets undergo a series of molts before becoming adults, then molting stops.

Try to use the smallest nymphs you can since they will be the youngest. At the conclusion of this investigation, return the nymphs to their home in the lab or classroom.

All aerobic organisms take in oxygen and give off carbon dioxide as long as they are alive. This is true for plants as well as animals. Some organisms have elaborate structures such as lungs or tracheal tubes for exchanging respiratory gases; others merely use moist membranes. If you place a living organism in a closed system, it is possible to measure its consumption of oxygen. To do this, you will need a respirometer, which you can easily construct.

Your first task will be to understand the operation of the respirometer. The second task will be to construct it.

Materials

- Large test tube
- Metric ruler
- Petroleum jelly (optional)
- House cricket nymphs (1g)
- One-hole stopper
- Beaker (100mL)
- Forceps
- Rigid polyethylene tubing or hollow glass tubing (20cm long) bent at a right angle
- Limewater
- Medicine dropper
- Support stand and clamp or several thick books
- Wad of cotton
- Glycerine
- Marking crayon
- Liquid detergent
- Balance
- Paper towels
- Spatula
- Transparent tape

(continued)

Respiration Lab #4

How Much Oxygen Do House Cricket Nymphs Consume in 15 Minutes? (continued)

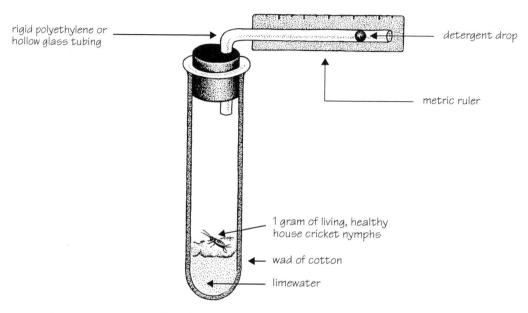

Respirometer containing house cricket nymphs

Procedure

1. Make the respirometer as shown in the diagram above. If you don't have a piece of tubing bent at a right angle as shown, you can use two pieces of straight tubing (one long and one short) connected by a piece of rubber tubing to form the right angle. There must be no air leaks in the respirometer. If you use the two pieces connected with a piece of rubber tubing, apply a small amount of petroleum jelly at the connecting points to ensure an airtight seal.

2. Pour a small amount of glycerine into the stopper hole. (The glycerine acts as a lubricant, making it easier to insert the tubing.) Insert the polyethylene or glass tubing into the one-hole stopper. If you are using glass, it is important to wrap a paper towel around the tubing to prevent injury if the glass breaks as you insert it.

(continued)

Respiration Lab #4

How Much Oxygen Do House Cricket Nymphs Consume in 15 Minutes? (continued)

3. With your marking crayon, draw a line 0.5cm above the bottom of the test tube. Add limewater to the tube until it is filled to the crayon mark. As any living organism in the tube uses oxygen, carbon dioxide will be excreted. The carbon dioxide will then be absorbed by the limewater, creating a slight vacuum in the respirometer. This partial vacuum will draw a drop of liquid detergent in the glass tubing *inward*. This movement will be measured in millimeters using a metric ruler taped to the glass tubing.

4. Place a wad of loose cotton on top of the limewater.

5. Weigh the beaker, then add 1g to its weight. Now add the nymphs, one by one, until you have 1 gram of live nymphs. You may not be able to get exactly 1 gram of nymphs. The mass of nymphs may weigh more than 1 gram; they may weigh 1.25g. This is not a problem. Merely divide the amount of detergent drop movement for each reading by 1.25. Place the nymphs on top of the cotton wad.

6. Tape the metric ruler to the tubing so that it looks like the diagram. With a medicine dropper, add a drop of detergent to the tubing. This drop should be near the end of the tubing (as shown).

7. Insert the stopper into the test tube. Do this *carefully*. Avoid spilling the detergent drop inside the tubing. Press down firmly on the stopper to make an airtight seal. If necessary, use a smear of petroleum jelly as a sealant on the rim of the test tube. Keep the setup in an upright position. It is best to use a support stand and clamps for this. If no support stand and clamps are available, stack several books as a support system. Don't move the setup once it is in place.

8. Wait five minutes before taking your initial reading. The CO_2 already inside the respirometer will be absorbed during this time.

9. Take the initial reading wherever the drop of detergent is with respect to the metric ruler after the five-minute waiting period. Always take your measurements using the same part of the detergent drop—for example, the left edge of the drop. Write down your initial reading in the table on the following page.

10. Take readings every minute for 15 minutes and record them in the data table.

(continued)

Respiration Lab #4

How Much Oxygen Do House Cricket Nymphs Consume in 15 Minutes? (continued)

DATA TABLE			
Initial reading: _____ (mm)			
Minute	Movement (mm)	Minute	Movement (mm)
1		9	
2		10	
3		11	
4		12	
5		13	
6		14	
7		15	
8			

Analysis

1. Is time of day a factor that affects the respiration rate of the cricket nymph?

       25 Low-Cost Biology Investigations

Name _____ Date _____

How Powerful Are Emerging Seedlings?

Introduction

Plants play a role in the breaking up of rock into smaller pieces. You may have observed this phenomenon if you have seen plants growing in sidewalk cracks. This investigation will focus on the ability of seedlings to break up solid materials.

You will also compare the relative strength of *monocotyledon* seedlings (grass and corn) to similar *dicotyledon* seedlings (lettuce and pea). There are two major differences between monocotyledon and dicotyledon plants: (1) monocotyledons have only one food leaf in their seeds, and (2) the veins in their leaves run parallel to each other. Dicotyledons have two food leaves in their seeds and the veins in their leaves look like a net.

In addition, you will investigate the relation between seed size and a seedling's ability to break through solid covering material of varying thicknesses and strengths. Grass and lettuce represent the small seeds whereas the corn and pea seeds are much larger. You may use any available variety of corn, grass, lettuce, or pea seeds, provided the seeds are fresh. In order of hardness, the covering materials are: plaster of paris, spackling paste, sand mix (cement). The sand mix is optional.

Materials

- Grass seeds*
- Corn seeds* (soak in water the night before planting)
- Pea seeds* (soak in water the night before planting)
- Lettuce seeds*
- Spackling paste

- Plaster of paris
- Sand mix** (concrete patching material)
- Spackling knife
- Fine-point permanent marker (waterproof)
- Paper towels or rags

- Trowel
- Newspaper
- Metric ruler
- Seed-starting mix
- Clear plastic cups approximately 9cm tall and 6cm wide (40)
- Water

*If sand mix is used, 81 seeds of each type are necessary; otherwise 54 seeds of each type are necessary.

**The use of sand mix is optional. If it is *not* used, only 28 containers will be needed.

(continued)

Seedling Power Lab

How Powerful Are Emerging Seedlings?
(continued)

Procedure

1. Using the permanent marker, label nine of the containers "Grass" (label only six containers if you are not using the sand mix). Print the letters near the bottom of the container, as shown in the diagram below. In a similar manner, print "Lettuce" on another set of containers, "Corn" on another set, and finally "Pea" on the last set of containers.

2. With the permanent marker, draw a line around the outside of each labeled container 6cm up from the bottom. See the diagram below.

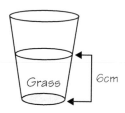

3. Label three corn containers "Plaster of paris." Print this label above or just below "Corn." Do the same for three of each of the other types of seed containers (three "Grass," three "Lettuce," and three "Pea").

4. In a similar manner, label three of the corn containers with "Spackling paste." Do the same to three of each of the other seed containers.

5. If you are using the sand mix, label the remaining seed containers "Sand mix." If you are not using sand mix, go on to step 6.

6. Separate the marked containers first by seed type and then by covering material.

(continued)

Seedling Power Lab

How Powerful Are Emerging Seedlings?
(continued)

7. Take one container marked "Plaster of paris" for each seed category and draw a line 0.5cm above the 6cm line.

8. Take another container marked "Plaster of paris" for each seed category and draw a line 1.0cm above the 6cm line.

9. Take the last container marked "Plaster of paris" for each seed category and draw a line 1.5cm above the 6cm line.

10. Repeat steps 7, 8, and 9; however, this time use the containers marked "Spackling paste."

11. If you are using the sand mix, mark these nine containers in the same manner as in steps 7, 8, and 9.

12. Spread out the newspaper so you won't make a mess when filling the containers. Use the trowel to fill each marked container with seed starting mix up to the 6cm line.

13. Plant nine seeds of the proper type in each marked container. Plant them according to the pattern shown in the diagram below.

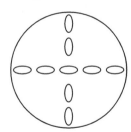

Plant the seeds as follows:

- Corn and peas—approximately 2cm deep. (It is best if the seeds are soaked in water the night before planting.)

- Grass and lettuce—just under the surface of the mix. (No presoaking is necessary.)

14. Water the contents thoroughly.

15. Read and follow the directions on the package of the covering materials. Use the unmarked containers for mixing the plaster of paris and the sand mix.

(continued)

Name _____ Date _____

How Powerful Are Emerging Seedlings?
(continued)

16. Cover the planted seeds with the appropriate material (plaster of paris, spackling paste, sand mix). Fill the containers to the height of the line *above* the 6cm line (0.5cm, 1cm, or 1.5cm). Use your spackling knife for this task. Be sure that the material covers all of the seed-starting mix and is in contact with the wall of each plastic container. Start with the spackling paste because it is easier to work with than the other two. Work quickly with the plaster of paris because it hardens in a very short time.

17. Set the containers aside for two days. On the third day examine each container's surface for cracks. Examine the starting mix to look for root growth that might be seen through the clear plastic walls of the containers. Make your observations for the next five days.

18. Record your observations in the following data table.

DATA TABLE		
Plaster of Paris	**Spackling Paste**	**Sand Mix**
Day 3		
Day 4		
Day 5		
Day 6		
Day 7		
Day 8		

(continued)

Seedling Power Lab

How Powerful Are Emerging Seedlings?
(continued)

Analysis

1. Which seeds broke through 0.5cm of the plaster of paris? _____
_____

2. Which seeds broke through 1.0cm of the plaster of paris? _____
_____

3. Which seeds broke through 1.5cm of the plaster of paris? _____
_____

4. Which seeds broke through 0.5cm of the spackling paste?_____
_____

5. Which seeds broke through 1.0cm of the spackling paste?_____
_____

6. Which seeds broke through 1.5cm of the spackling paste?_____
_____

7. Which seeds broke through 0.5cm of the sand mix?_____
_____

8. Which seeds broke through 1.0cm of the sand mix?_____
_____

9. Which seeds broke through 1.5cm of the sand mix?_____
_____

(continued)

Seedling Power Lab

How Powerful Are Emerging Seedlings?
(continued)

10. Which seeds showed the greatest amount of root growth? _____

    _____

    _____

11. Which seeds showed the least seed growth? _____

    _____

    _____

12. Are dicotyledonous seedlings stronger than monocotyledonous seedlings?_____

    Justify your answer: _____

    _____

    _____

    _____

13. The larger the seed, the more powerful the seedling. Is this generalization true or false?

    Justify your answer: _____

    _____

    _____

    _____

For Further Investigation

1. Repeat this investigation using seeds that produce seedlings with thick stems.
   Squash and cucumber seeds are two examples of this type. Are these seedlings able
   to break through thicker layers of covering material than the seedlings just used? Is
   there a relationship between the thickness of a seedling's stem and its ability to
   break through a hard covering material?

     25 Low-Cost Biology Investigations

Spider Lab #1

How Are Spiders Different from Insects?

Introduction

When most people hear the word "spider," they usually wrinkle their faces in disgust and say "Ugh!" What spiders really need is a good public relations person to improve their image. All spiders are carnivores and they almost always feed on insects, which is good for us. Only a few species are dangerous; most spiders are not capable of penetrating our skin even if they tried to bite us. However, the poison glands of the female black widow spider contain a nerve poison; this spider's bite is extremely painful and, in a few cases, deadly. The males, on the other hand, are harmless.

Spiders belong to the class of arthropods named *arachnids*. All members of this class live on land and breathe air. With this as background information, we can compare spiders with insects.

Materials

- Hand lens
- Cricket, or written observations of cricket anatomy
- Preserved spider
- Dissecting pan
- Forceps
- Paper towels

Procedure

1. Using forceps, grasp the preserved spider by a walking leg. Place the spider in the dissecting pan. There is a diagram at the end of the Observations section to help you find the spider's structures. Use the diagram only if necessary or at the conclusion of your observations to confirm your work. After making a spider observation, observe the analogous part of a cricket (or refer to your notes) so that a comparison can be made between the two organisms. Record the differences in the space provided after question 2 in the Analysis section.

(continued)

Spider Lab #1

How Are Spiders Different from Insects?
(continued)

Observations

1. Observe the second pair of appendages. Describe them: _____

   _____

2. Use the hand lens to find the poison gland openings located near the tips of the
   claws. Can you find them?_____
   Describe them:_____

   _____

3. Locate the mouth between the first appendages. Examine the mouth using your
   magnifying lens. Can you determine how the spider eats? _____

   _____

4. Where are the eyes located? How many eyes does your specimen have?_____
   Spiders have poor vision despite having a number of simple eyes. Since they lack
   antennae and have poor eyesight, sensory hairs provide the spider with information
   about changes in its environment. On what part or parts of its body are sensory
   hairs to be found? _____

   _____

5. How does the *posterior* (rear) section of the spider's body differ from the *anterior*
   (front) section?_____
   The two sections of the body are separated by a deep groove called a *pedicel*.

6. Look at the third pair of appendages. Compare them in size and shape to the first
   pair and to the pairs of walking legs that are behind the third pair: _____

   _____

(continued)

Spider Lab #1

How Are Spiders Different from Insects?
(continued)

7. How many pairs of walking legs does your spider have? _____

8. With the hand lens, search the rear *ventral* (under) side of the abdomen for web-spinning apparatuses called *spinnerets*. You may also find the spider's breathing apparatus—a *book lung*—on the ventral side of the abdomen in front of the spinnerets. Describe either or both of these types of special structures, if you found them:

_____

_____

Typical spider

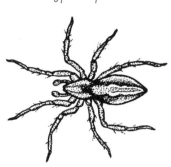

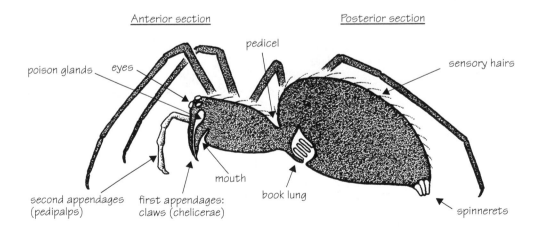

Anterior section   Posterior section

pedicel

poison glands   eyes

sensory hairs

mouth

second appendages (pedipalps)   first appendages: claws (chelicerae)

book lung

spinnerets

(continued)

25 Low-Cost Biology Investigations

Spider Lab #1

How Are Spiders Different from Insects?
(continued)

Analysis

1. How is the spider adapted for capturing insects? _____

   _____

   _____

   _____

   _____

   _____

   _____

   _____

   _____

   _____

2. How do spiders differ from insects such as crickets? _____

   _____

   _____

   _____

   _____

   _____

   _____

   _____

   _____

   _____

   _____

   _____

Spider Lab #2

How Do Spider Webs Trap Insects?

Introduction

Not all spiders spin webs. Many spiders hunt their prey; others lie in wait near flowers for insects (their main food supply) to wander by.

There are many kinds of webs, but only a few basic types will be mentioned in this investigation: *sheet*, *dome*, and *orb*. Each has a distinctive shape. The sheet web, as you would suspect from its name, looks like a flat sheet and is constructed horizontally. The dome web looks like a dome, rising upward and outward. The orb web consists of a series of circles and is built to hang vertically. (Orb means circle.)

House spiders spin a sheet web. This type of web has a living area that looks like a small bag in the farthest corner. This is attached to the web, which is really a sheet of spun silk covered with trip lines. If an insect touches a trip line, a vibration is sent to the living area and the spider is able to determine where its prey is located on the web. Sheet webs of this type are relatively simple since the web neither traps the insect in a fine mass of threads nor glues the insect to sticky threads.

Some spiders spin webs of fine silk that ensnare any insect that lands upon them. Other spiders spin webs of sticky threads which have tiny droplets of adhesive along their length. This last type is the most efficient for trapping insects. Some spiders construct a new web each night, eating the material that made up the old web before starting the new one.

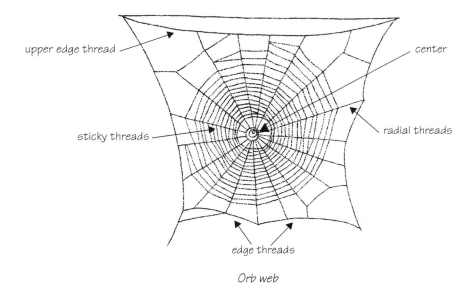

Orb web

(continued)

Spider Lab #2

How Do Spider Webs Trap Insects? (continued)

Materials

- Several cotton swabs
- Book or paper for keeping records
- Illuminated microscope (20X–30X) (optional)
- Metric ruler
- Pencil or pen
- Hand lens

Procedure

1. Locate a spider's web, preferably an orb web. Look in a garden or vacant lot in which plants are growing—anywhere insects would come to feed. If you live in the city and there are no parks or lots with plants nearby, you should still be able to find spiders, even if you live in an apartment. Perhaps you won't find an orb web; more likely it will be a small sheet web. Look under hanging cabinets, in out-of-the-way corners that are overlooked when cleaning, and in the basement. Work with whatever web you happen to find.

2. Bring your ruler close to, but not touching, the web. Make and record approximate measurements of length and width. Length: _____ Width: _____

3. Record the number and kinds (if you can identify them) of insects that are trapped in the web: _____

   _____

4. If the spider is visible, use your hand lens for a magnified view. Describe the spider in words, including size, color, and any other information that you feel is important:

   _____

   _____

   _____

   _____

(continued)

Spider Lab #2

How Do Spider Webs Trap Insects? (continued)

5. In the space below, make a sketch of the web. This sketch will become a web map, so do a good job. Your web need not be the actual size of the original, but the threads and their spatial relations are important. On the line below the sketch, indicate if it is a sheet, dome, or orb web.

_____ *web map*

6. Examine the web. This step, as well as steps 7 and 8, refers to an orb web. (If you have found a sheet or dome web, ignore these steps and go on to step 9.) Find the upper edge thread at the top of the web. Label it on your web map.

7. Find and label the center threads, which are quite close together near the center of the web. There may a number of center threads—six or more.

8. The radial threads run from the center to the edges of the web. Identify them and label several radial threads on your map.

(continued)

Spider Lab #2

How Do Spider Webs Trap Insects? (continued)

9. Take a cotton swab and gently touch threads in different regions of the web. Where are the threads that are sticky with adhesive droplets? _____

_____

Where are the safe, dry threads along which the spider moves? _____

_____

It is important not to be trapped in one's own web! Complete the web map, indicating the location of the safe threads and the sticky ones.

10. Examine the sticky threads with your magnifier. Look for tiny droplets of adhesive material at various points along the sticky threads. When you find one, touch a droplet with a cotton swab. What did you observe? _____

_____

_____

_____

_____

11. If possible, find a different type of web, preferably a sheet or dome web. Make a map of that web. Compare this web with the first one you mapped.

Analysis

1. How are the two web maps similar?

2. How do the maps differ?

3. Why is silk important for the survival of spiders?

Vinegar Eel Lab #1

Are Vinegar Eels Attracted to Light?

Introduction

Have you ever seen a vinegar eel in a bottle of cider vinegar? Most likely not. You might be surprised to learn that tiny round worms, commonly called vinegar eels (*Turbatrix aceti* [*Anguillula*]), are found in untreated vinegar and are a problem for vinegar producers. You won't find them in the vinegar sold in your local supermarket because that vinegar has been pasteurized. Actually, vinegar eels don't consume the vinegar itself; rather they feed on the vinegar bacteria living in the cider vinegar.

There are many reasons to select vinegar eels for biological investigations. They are harmless, nonparasitic roundworms that are large enough to be seen with your eyes, if the culture medium in which they are living is held up to a bright light. The adult females are about 2mm in length whereas the males are a little smaller, measuring less than 1.5mm long. Only simple equipment and supplies are required to maintain them. Their hardiness is an advantage for the investigator. They will survive and reproduce if the temperature of their environment is between 20°C and 30°C and if the pH is no less than 2 or greater than 10.

Since these creatures are transparent, you can see all their internal organs with a low-power microscope or a hand-held magnifier. The eggs of the vinegar eel are fertilized internally and develop in the uterus of the females. Forty or more eggs are normally produced by each female. The normal life span of a vinegar eel is slightly less than a year, averaging ten months. The picture below will give you a good idea of their internal structure.

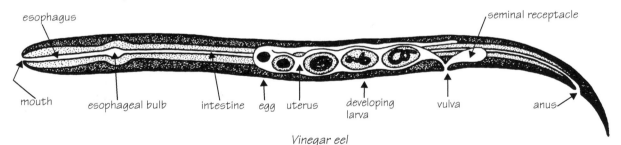

Vinegar eel

For some reason, vinegar eels crowd together just under the surface of the cider vinegar in which they are living. There are a number of possible reasons for this behavior. One possibility is that they come to the surface for oxygen. Another possibility is that they are attracted to the light. Can you think of any other possibilities?

In this investigation you will attempt to find out if light is the stimulus to which the vinegar eels respond by gathering at the surface of their culture medium.

(continued)

Vinegar Eel Lab #1

Are Vinegar Eels Attracted to Light?
(continued)

Materials

- Small plastic juice bottles or jars (4)
- Vinegar eels
- Apple cider
- Hand magnifier
- Transparent tape

- Small test tubes and stoppers (3)
- Scissors
- Cider vinegar (*without preservatives*)
- Cotton plugs for bottles

- Medicine droppers (or pipets)
- Graduated cylinder (10mL)
- Metric ruler
- Black construction paper

Procedure

1. Thoroughly wash, rinse, and dry the plastic juice bottles or jars. Three of these are your culture containers.

2. Using the graduated cylinder, add 60mL of apple cider to each of the three containers.

3. Next add 40mL of cider vinegar to each of the three bottles. Your culture medium is now ready.

4. From time to time, you will have to add new culture medium to replace the medium that has evaporated. Fill a fourth clean jar that has a screw-on top with 240mL of apple cider and 160mL of cider vinegar. This is your jar of replacement medium.

5. Using the medicine dropper or pipet, add 15 to 20 drops of the vinegar eel culture to each culture container.

6. Insert a cotton plug in each bottle to keep dust and dirt out while allowing air to enter.

7. After the eels have become accustomed to their new homes, take your hand magnifier and observe where most of the eels are located in the containers. Where did you observe most of them to be? _____

(continued)

Vinegar Eel Lab #1

Are Vinegar Eels Attracted to Light?
(continued)

8. Transfer the culture medium and vinegar eels into three test tubes so they are about three quarters full.

9. Leave one tube upright in sunlight or artificial light. This tube is the control.

10. Completely cover the second tube with black construction paper to seal out all light. Use transparent tape to hold the construction paper in place.

11. Wrap the third tube with the black construction paper just as you did with the second tube, but this time use scissors to cut a window—approximately 2cm square—near the bottom of the third test tube.

12. Shine a strong light from a lamp or halogen bulb flashlight into the window of the third tube for five minutes.

13. At the end of the five-minute interval, quickly remove the construction paper and observe where most of the vinegar eels are located. Record this information in the data table below.

14. Next remove the black paper from the second test tube. Note the location of the main mass of vinegar eels. Do the same for the first test tube. Write your results in the table.

DATA TABLE	
Test Tube	**Location of the Main Body of Vinegar Eels**
#1	
#2	
#3	

Analysis

1. On the basis of your experiment, are vinegar eels attracted to the light? Justify your answer.

Vinegar Eel Lab #2

Do Vinegar Eels Respond Negatively
to Gravity?

Introduction

Vinegar eels gather under the medium surface in their culture container. In this investigation you will hypothesize that the stimulus for this behavior is a negative response to gravity.

Materials

- Vinegar eels
- Apple cider
- Hand magnifier
- Clear flexible plastic tubing (bore = ¼ inch*, 1 foot* in length)
- Small plastic juice bottles or jars (4)
- Small test tubes and stoppers (3)
- Scissors
- Cider vinegar (*without preservatives*)
- Cotton plugs for bottles
- Book or wood block
- Rubber bands
- Medicine droppers (or pipets)
- Graduated cylinder (10mL)
- Metric ruler
- Black construction paper or cloth
- Clock or watch
- Transparent tape

*Plastic tubing is measured in English units rather than metric units.

Procedure

1. Cut the plastic tubing into three equal pieces.

2. Prepare culture containers and culture medium as follows:

    a. Thoroughly wash, rinse, and dry the plastic juice bottles or jars. Three of these are your culture containers.

    b. Using the graduated cylinder, add 60mL of apple cider to each of the three containers.

(continued)

     25 Low-Cost Biology Investigations

Do Vinegar Eels Respond Negatively to Gravity? (continued)

    c. Next add 40mL of cider vinegar to each of the three bottles. Your culture medium is now ready.

    d. From time to time you will have to add new culture medium to replace the medium that has evaporated. Fill the fourth clean jar, which has a screw-on top, with 240mL of apple cider and 160mL of cider vinegar. This is your jar of replacement medium.

    e. Using the medicine dropper or pipet, add 15 to 20 drops of the vinegar eel culture to each culture container.

    f. Insert a cotton plug in each bottle to keep dust and dirt out while allowing air to enter.

3. Seal one end of each piece of tubing by folding over 2cm at the end. Hold the folded ends in place with rubber bands to prevent leaking. Fill each piece of tubing with vinegar eels and culture medium. Strive to have as little air as possible in the tubing. Having only liquid in the tubing would be best. Seal the other ends of the tubing.

4. Form a loop of each piece of tubing by bringing the ends together to form a circle. Use your transparent tape to keep the circle intact.

5. Stand one circle upright as shown in diagram A. Rest the second piece of tubing against a book or block of wood at a 45° angle, as in diagram B. Place the third circle of tubing flat on the table top as in diagram C.

    A   B   C

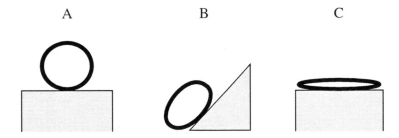

6. Cover the three circles of tubing with black paper or cloth to eliminate light as a factor.

(continued)

Vinegar Eel Lab #2

Do Vinegar Eels Respond Negatively
to Gravity? (continued)

7. Wait ten minutes, then remove the cloth or paper. Use your hand lens to locate the vinegar eels in each piece of tubing. Are most of the eels closer to the top surface of each piece of tubing?_____

_____

_____

_____

Where are most of them located in each case? _____

_____

_____

_____

_____

_____

_____

_____

_____

Analysis

1. Is gravity a stimulus for vinegar eels? Justify your answer.

Index

A

adult house crickets, 62–66
air temperature, 48
arachnids, 77

B

balance, 19–20
Brassica rapa seeds, 54

C

cider vinegar, 85, 89
control (experimental), 5, 27, 32

D

dandelions, 5
   flower heads, 1, 8–11, 12–15
   scape, 1
   seeds, 5, 54

E

earthworms, 16–18
equilibrium, 19, 20
exercise and muscle strength, 36
eyes, 19, 20

F

fatigue, 36, 38
florets, 9, 13
fruits (dandelion seeds), 5–6

G

germinating seeds, 51–54
germination, 5–7
gravity, vinegar eel reaction to, 88

H

house cricket nymphs, 67–70
hypothermia, 56

I

insects, trapping in webs, 81

L

land crustaceans, 58–61
   observing, 55–57
lettuce seeds, 6
light, 8, 11, 12, 14, 16, 17
   vinegar eel attraction to, 85

M, N

muscle strength, 36–38, 39–40
nymphs, 67, 69, 70

O

oil, 44
oil-soaked feathers and body temperature, 48–50
oil spills
   cleaning up, 43–45
   effects on sea birds, 46–47
oxygen, use of by seeds, 51